Darwin's South America

ALSO BY ROBERT S. HOPKINS

Island of the Deep Sea (with Albert B. Carr)

Darwin's
South America

ROBERT S. HOPKINS

ILLUSTRATED

The John Day Company

NEW YORK

PRINTED IN THE UNITED STATES OF AMERICA
Library of Congress Catalogue Card Number: 69-10815

Contents

Illustrations

6

7

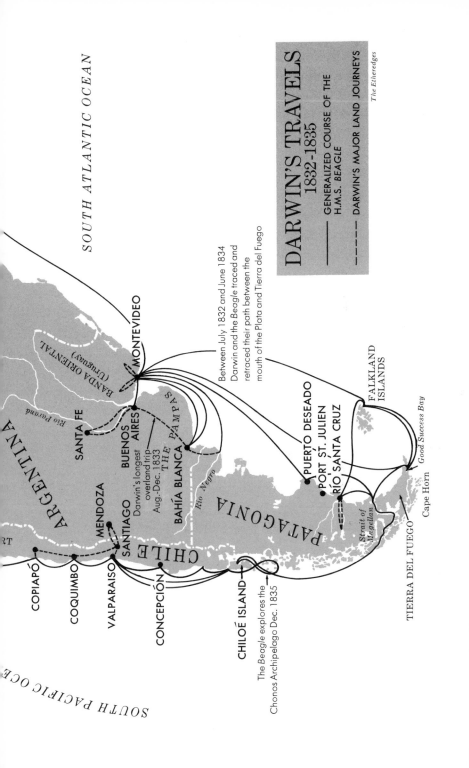

SOUTH ATLANTIC OCEAN

SOUTH PACIFIC OCEAN

DARWIN'S TRAVELS
1832-1835

—— GENERALIZED COURSE OF THE H.M.S. BEAGLE

------ DARWIN'S MAJOR LAND JOURNEYS

The Etheredges

Between July 1832 and June 1834 Darwin and the Beagle traced and retraced their path between the mouth of the Plata and Tierra del Fuego

MONTEVIDEO

BANDA ORIENTAL (Uruguay)

Rio Paraná

ARGENTINA

SANTA FE

BUENOS AIRES

Darwin's longest overland trip—Aug.-Dec. 1833

THE PAMPAS

BAHÍA BLANCA

Rio Negro

PATAGONIA

PUERTO DESEADO

PORT ST. JULIEN

RÍO SANTA CRUZ

FALKLAND ISLANDS

Good Success Bay

Strait of Magellan

TIERRA DEL FUEGO

Cape Horn

MENDOZA

SANTIAGO

CHILE

COPIAPÓ

COQUIMBO

VALPARAISO

CONCEPCIÓN

CHILOÉ ISLAND

The Beagle explores the Chonos Archipelago Dec. 1835

RT

Preface

FOR Charles Darwin to gain the position of naturalist aboard H.M.S. *Beagle* at the age of twenty-two was a magnificent stroke of luck.

The year was 1831, and the *Beagle* was bound on a charting expedition to the coast of South America. Twice the position of naturalist had been offered to older, more experienced men. And twice it had been reluctantly declined. Even after the offer was made to Darwin, the help of a sympathetic uncle was needed to convince Darwin's father that the voyage would not corrupt his son.

As it turned out, the elder Darwin's fear that the voyage might change young Charles proved not entirely groundless. The voyage lasted longer than anyone anticipated, a few months short of five years. The *Beagle* eventually circled the globe, calling at exotic and little-known places like Tahiti, New Zealand, and Keeling Island in the Indian Ocean. But three and a half years of the voyage were spent in South America.

From England, the *Beagle* sailed first to Brazil, then south along the expanse of coast to Tierra del Fuego, and finally north again on the west coast to Peru and the Galápagos Islands. At the time, South America was less explored than Africa or Asia. It was a continent everywhere a frontier. Portions were totally unknown while other regions were roamed by Indians that fought all invaders. The wars of independence which freed the countries of South America from Spain and Portugal had been fought only scant years before, and these first years without a king had turned out to be incredibly chaotic. Everyday life was simple and raw. Revolution was common. Death and governmental corruption were as accepted as courtesy toward strangers and the enjoyment of a good meal. In such a setting, the voyage was bound to have its impact on Darwin.

But the resulting changes in Darwin could never have been anticipated by even his father. In one sense the voyage made a man of him. He left England with his ambitions and talents undiscovered. He returned confident he could be happy dedicating his life to science. And in South America he uncovered facts that eventually led to his revolutionary theories on evolution. More than forty years later —long after the success of the *Origin of Species* —Darwin wrote that the voyage aboard the *Beagle* was the most important event of his life. Darwin additionally felt that the voyage provided his first disciplined scientific training. He always believed his skill as an observer was one of the major reasons for his success as a scientist, and it was a skill sharpened in South America.

During the voyage he entered meticulous descriptions of plants, animals, and the land in a series of notebooks. He recorded daily life afloat and ashore in a long diary. Still more anecdotes and news of his discoveries filled his letters home. In all his writing, the human landscape was no less subject to Darwin's impartial eye than was the natural one; his description of the gaucho is as vivid and precise as the buzzard.

He saw the beginnings of great cities, the way of life on sprawling cattle ranches, the brutal treatment of Indians in Andean copper mines. Such observations share equal detail in his writing with fossils and geology, bugs and finches. What may surprise the reader is that so much of what Darwin saw has relevance to South America today. In the 1830's it was very much a land that foretold what it was to become.

Here then is a view of an exciting continent portrayed by one of history's most scrupulous observers. It is also a look at Darwin's discoveries on the land and in himself that led to his momentous book the *Origin of Species.* The excerpts of Darwin's writing are taken from his diary, letters, and the 1860 edition of the *Voyage of the Beagle.* If a little of the good-natured youth destined to become one of the catalytic forces of history can be seen in these writings too, so much the better.

PROLOGUE

The Expedition of 1826

THE CURIOUS preface to Darwin's journey to South America began while he was a struggling medical student at Edinburgh in the year 1826. Captain Philip King's expedition sailed that year to explore and chart South America's southern coasts, especially the bleak land's end of Tierra del Fuego. For the British Admiralty there was nothing unusual about the King expedition. The great era of discovery had ended with the voyages of Captain Cook a half century before, leaving the explorers of the nineteenth century to fill in the map with less spectacular but more detailed surveys. Mounting only two ships, the H.M.S. *Adventure* and a smaller brig, the H.M.S. *Beagle,* the King expedition was typical of the time.

Forty years earlier King's expedition would have been nearly impossible. The heart of Spain's empire lay in

South America, and its jealousy toward those who wished to meddle in the affairs of the already restless colonies was only too apparent. Even on such an innocent mission, British ships cruising the South America coast would have been suspect of more serious intentions. Their sighting by a coastal village remembering the exploits of Sir Francis Drake would probably have provoked a more dramatic reaction: a sounded warning, the cry of pirates, and the villagers fleeing with their prized possessions to the interior.

If not an act of war or piracy, a British expedition prior to the turn of the eighteenth century would at the least have been thought of as curious. South America was then a continent sparsely populated around the edges. The interior of the Amazon Basin and the windswept plateaus of Patagonia were almost completely unknown. The French had hastily mapped the Strait of Magellan in 1796. But for one and all, the stormy southern coasts of South America were something to be bypassed as quickly as possible. The southernmost region, the jagged islands of Tierra del Fuego, was so valueless as to be in truth the end of the earth.

But things were to change long before the King expedition sailed. Between 1810 and 1825 all the former Portuguese and Spanish colonies in South America shook the bonds of their rulers. The former Spanish colonies fought long, bloody wars for independence. Brazil slipped away from Portugal without firing a shot. Waiting and encouraging all the while was England.

Since defeating the French and Spanish fleets at Trafalgar in 1805, England had become undisputed master of the seas. Feeling their power, the British began probing every corner of the earth for places to export manufactured goods in exchange for the wheat, cotton, and beef needed by the island kingdom. Parts of South America were indeed inviting.

The first two decades of the 1800's found the British doing what they could to hasten the already loosening bonds between the colonies and Spain and Portugal. In 1806 England went so far as to mount a halfhearted, unsuccessful expedition to occupy Buenos Aires, the key to the potentially rich cattlelands of the Pampas. When the Portuguese royal family, fleeing Napoleon's armies in 1807, moved the capital of the empire to Brazil, royalty, entourage, and treasury were escorted by British warships; when the doors opened for trade with Brazil the following year, first and best able to step in was England.

When the South American wars of revolution came, many former British soldiers, jobless after Napoleon's defeat, joined the revolutionary armies. Five thousand English, Irish, and Scottish fought with Simón Bolívar. British merchants were quick to supply armies with uniforms and arms. A Scotsman, Lord Cochrane, commanded the revolutionaries' fleet in the Pacific that helped liberate Chile and Peru. Then, his reputation awesome by that time, he sailed to the east coast and literally frightened the Portuguese Navy away from Brazil. Following independence, both England and the United States stated they would not tolerate interference with the new nations, and the British fleet stood ready to back up this intention.

By 1826 Britain's commercial interest in South America was immense. Backed by a large measure of commercial self-concern, charting and mapping expeditions became a proper activity for the British Admiralty. Even Tierra del Fuego by 1826 had taken on a new value. With trade rapidly developing between England and the west coast of South America, Tierra del Fuego was a corner that had to be rounded. The turn of the century, too, had brought the discovery of new whaling grounds in the Pacific Ocean. Both British and American whalers out of Plymouth and New Bedford found battling the stormy seas near Tierra del Fuego a necessity as they made for the islands of the Pacific and the whaling grounds nearby. Still, until the King expedition, the myriad islands and numerous channels of Tierra del Fuego had never been fully explored or accurately charted.

Had Charles Darwin heard of the sailing of King's expedition, he undoubtedly would have given it only passing notice, occupied as he was with his own problem of academic survival. Nor was it likely that he or many other Englishmen paid close attention to the return of the *Adventure* and *Beagle* to England four years later, in October, 1830. Most of the expedition's time had been spent charting Tierra del Fuego's endless channels and fog-shrouded coasts. It had been a slow, tedious task, one not entirely successful. There was not enough time to explore every inlet and channel, though some of them might have provided shorter routes from the Atlantic to the Pacific. Great lengths of coast had been ignored. There had been the loss of several auxiliary boats and the death of several crewmen from accident and disease. But such losses were expected. What was unexpected, however, was the death of the *Beagle*'s commander, Pringle Stokes.

In August, 1828, Stokes and the *Beagle* joined up with the *Adventure* after a difficult survey of the southern coasts of Chile. The monotony and boredom of the craggy, gray coasts had thrown Stokes into a depression, and he fell ill soon after his rendezvous with the *Adventure*. Depression and sickness finally drove him to suicide. Stokes' death inadvertently played a role in Darwin's story. Later that year, twenty-four-year-old Robert Fitz-Roy was appointed captain of the *Beagle*. FitzRoy continued the survey with authority and skill, earning for himself in a short time a reputation as an accurate surveyor and efficient seaman. FitzRoy had his own taste of the voyage's bad luck when he found himself burdened with four primitive Indians from Tierra del Fuego, taken the previous February as hostages to exchange for a stolen whaleboat. Unable to recover the whaleboat, he ended up with no better solution than to bring them back to England. When the second expedition was decided, FitzRoy had already made plans to take the Indians back to Tierra del Fuego at his own expense. One had soon died of smallpox, but the remaining three he had housed and educated.

FitzRoy's own talent and the help of an influential relative put him in command of the second expedition, and the *Beagle* was recommissioned. The idea of taking a naturalist was his. As he later wrote, his experience on the first voyage made him "anxious that no opportunity of collecting useful information during the voyage should be lost." FitzRoy made a request to Captain Francis Beaufort, the Admiralty hydrographer for a "well-educated and scientific person . . . to profit by the opportunity of visiting distant countries yet little known." Then with the search for a naturalist started, he began supervising reconstruction and refitting of the *Beagle.*

Beaufort turned to the Cambridge astronomer George Peacock for advice. The second voyage of the *Beagle* would probably be longer than the first. After completing a survey of portions of coast from Brazil to Tierra del Fuego, then north to Peru, the *Beagle* was to strike out across the Pacific, making a series of chronometer measurements around the entire globe. To find the right man for such a lengthy voyage would be difficult.

Peacock first wrote to a colleague at Cambridge, the botanist John Henslow, suggesting Henslow's brother-in-law, the naturalist Leonard Jenyns. Of course, the position carried no salary, and the quarters would be cramped. Still it was a rare opportunity. Jenyns considered the offer, was on the verge of accepting, then declined.

Henslow very nearly went himself. The misery reflected on Mrs. Henslow's face was enough, however, to end his thoughts of accepting the offer.

But Henslow had another recommendation. There was a student of his, a young man named Charles Darwin. He wasn't a finished naturalist to be sure, far from it. Yet Henslow felt he had a number of admirable qualifications. Peacock agreed with Henslow's recommendation. Both wrote to young Darwin, who was finishing that summer at home in Shrewsbury, about the position open aboard the *Beagle.* It was August, 1831.

1

Darwin and FitzRoy

IF DARWIN had been judged solely on his record as a student, there was absolutely nothing that would have justified Henslow's faith in him. His academic career from beginning to end was barely mediocre. Darwin's famous grandfather, Erasmus Darwin, had been a wealthy physician, author, poet, and scientist. His father, Robert Darwin, was himself a strong individualist and a prominent doctor in the village of Shrewsbury. Though not a noble family, the Darwins were well able to provide a proper education for their children. Yet after his first year at day school, Charles' teachers felt he was far slower than his younger sister Catherine.

Following day school, he entered the Shrewsbury Grammar School. Like most schools of the time, its courses were mainly classical. Darwin later considered the seven years he studied there a total loss. Apparently his masters felt the same. He was considered a very ordinary boy, and his father was forced to admit that young Charles probably had an intellect below average.

Even during those first years of school Darwin's education came from outside of the classroom. Before the age of eight he had "the passion for collecting which leads a man to be a systematic naturalist, a virtuoso, or a miser. . . ." Pebbles, plants, birds eggs, or seashells, it didn't matter. He combed the forests and fields near Shrewsbury for anything that interested him, and if he could catch a rat or two along the way, so much the better. To the lectures in classical geography at Shrewsbury Charles preferred helping his older brother Erasmus, named after their grandfather, perform chemistry experiments in the garden tool shed. They worked hard together, and Darwin read a number of books on chemistry. Later he felt that no school experience had given him so real an understanding of experimental science.

During his last years at Shrewsbury, after Erasmus had gone on to Cambridge, Darwin's interest in the world he could see and gather became well developed. When Erasmus was enrolled at Edinburgh to study medicine, their father, feeling that more time at Shrewsbury was doing little good, enrolled Charles also. Like the rest of the Darwin men, he would make a tolerably fine doctor.

At Edinburgh his interest in formal education ran true to form. Darwin plunged into the system, which consisted of lectures from eight in the morning until early evening. But the classes on anatomy and geology were stifling. His memories of the infirmary's operating theater in the days before chloroform made him seriously doubt his stomach's ability to take doctoring as a profession. He soon found himself missing lectures to wander among the shelves of books in the library, or to take long walks through the rolling countryside, or to search for specimens along the seashore. With local fishermen he learned how to catch marine animals, and he paid a taxidermist, who had been to the jungles of Brazil with the explorer Watertown, to teach him to stuff animals.

Though not an exciting place to spend one's teens, Darwin made the best of what Edinburgh had to offer him. He joined the Plinean Society, which met frequently in a basement room to discuss informal papers on natural science. One winter the American artist and ornithologist John J. Audubon was the rage of Edinburgh society, giving lectures and displaying his drawings while dressed in the frontier garb of the American West. Darwin saw him once demonstrate his technique for stuffing birds. At another scientific meeting he heard the famous explorer Sir Walter Scott. For young Darwin, sitting in a classroom listening to a droning lecture, compared with the world of action and deeds, was dull indeed.

In April, 1827, sensing Darwin's apathy toward medicine, his father withdrew him from Edinburgh. The following October he entered Christ's College at Cambridge in preparation for what was likely to be the only gentleman's profession left open to him, the ministry. He was to spend the next three years at Cambridge.

The years at Cambridge were happy ones, if not productive on the surface. Darwin tried lectures on math and, much to his admitted regret later in life, found he learned very slowly. Darwin still found more excitement outside the classroom and later remembered that most of his lectures at Cambridge had as little effect on him as those at Edinburgh or Shrewsbury. It was probably his second cousin, William Darwin Fox, also a Cambridge student, who convinced him to attend the botany lectures of John Stevens Henslow, and from then on Darwin's life in school acquired a new dimension. Henslow was a kind of scientist fast disappearing, knowledgeable in half a dozen natural sciences, including botany, zoology, and geology. He was an exciting lecturer, which for Darwin must have been a startling contrast with his years at Edinburgh. Like many of the professors at Cambridge, Henslow's views toward science and the world were unbendingly orthodox, tempered by the theological orientation of the studies at Cambridge. But he was known for his patience and interest in those students worthy of it. His weekly openhouse, where students could meet and talk with noted scientists of the day, was famous.

Before long, Darwin became a regular attendant at Henslow's gatherings, and in his third year at Cambridge, Henslow became his tutor. Darwin always felt that Henslow sensed something unusual in him that he himself wasn't aware of. Henslow encouraged Darwin to study geology, despite his first discouraging contact with it at Edinburgh. He introduced him to the eloquent geologist Adam Sedgwick, who would later give Darwin a feel for unraveling the geological landscape. First as guide and teacher, later as trusted friend and encouraging colleague,

Henslow was an influence that changed the direction of Darwin's life.

But at Cambridge, too, Darwin was the same young man. His love of the outdoors drew him to a group that liked to ride, shoot, and enjoy long dinners taken at country inns. Darwin rode well and boldly. By anyone's measure he was a crack shot, and later, aboard the *Beagle,* he once brought down twenty-three snipes with twenty-four shots. He was so fond of the sporting life that one of his father's worst fears was that he would, in the language of the day, end up an idler.

Far from it. Every holiday Darwin spent hiking and collecting. These sports and the hours he spent with Henslow were his only escape from the boredom and routine of college life. Years later he wrote:

But no pursuit at Cambridge was followed with nearly so much eagerness or gave me so much pleasure as collecting beetles. It was the mere passion for collecting, for I did not dissect them, and rarely compared their external characters with published descriptions, but got them named anyhow. I will give a proof of my zeal: one day, on tearing off some old bark, I saw two rare beetles, and seized one in each hand; then I saw a third and new kind, which I could not bear to lose, so that I popped the one which I held in my right hand into my mouth. Alas it ejected some intensely acrid fluid, which burnt my tongue so that I was forced to spit the beetle out, which was lost, as was the third one.

During his last year at Cambridge, Darwin discovered Alexander von Humboldt. Thirty years before, as a young naturalist, Humboldt had spent five years exploring northern South America, Mexico, and Cuba. Humboldt personified the gentleman scientist of the 1700's, knowledgeable in nearly every science of the day, and with enough money to do what he wanted. Instead of specializing in one science, his desire was to illustrate a unity in all nature. Humboldt's demonic drive and energy set him apart from the rest. During his five years in what was then the Spanish Empire, Humboldt explored the Orinoco River, hiked the old Inca trail along Andean plateaus, climbed Mount Chimborazo, then thought to be the world's highest peak, described the habits of Indians, deplored slavery in Cuba, surveyed silver mines in Mexico, and pondered the idea of a canal across the Isthmus of Panama. News of Humboldt's deeds preceded his arrival to the scientific circles of Paris. In the first decades of the 1800's he was nearly as famous as Napoleon. When Humboldt's *Personal Narratives,* the book which described his adventures, was published, it became a best seller. The impact of reading Humboldt's impressions of a continent almost unchronicled in science had a profound effect on Darwin, and he often reread Humboldt's moving descriptions of South America.

In April, 1831, twenty-two-year-old Charles Darwin earned his degree without honors from Cambridge, though he still had two semesters to remain in residence before taking his orders as a clergyman. In the months following his degree he was a lost soul. The thought of becoming a country parson left him uneasy, though he had no alternative to propose for what to do with his life.

At Henslow's suggestion he returned to Edinburgh for several lectures in geology. As a result of reading Humboldt, he thought he might journey to Tenerife, in the Canary Islands, and went so far as to study Spanish and look into ship passage. That summer Adam Sedgwick asked him to go along on a brief geological study of North Wales. Again at Henslow's urging, he accepted.

One incident that preceded the trip may have been Darwin's beginning as a scientist. Sedgwick arrived at Darwin's home to spend a night with his family before they left for Wales. Shortly before, a workman in a quarry had discovered a tropical shell embedded in the gravel, which, if it had not recently fallen into the pit, was quite a geological find. Darwin enthusiastically reported the discovery to Sedgwick, who, to his surprise, took the news rather glumly. Sedgwick dismissed the whole subject by saying that if the shell were authentic, it would be a great misfortune to geology, for it would go against all that was known about the geologic deposits of the Midlands. It was a moment of discovery for Darwin. Later he wrote: "Nothing before had ever made me thoroughly realise, though I had read various scientific books, that science consists in grouping facts so that general laws or conclusions may be drawn from them."

He returned from Wales in late August to find a letter from George Peacock with an enclosure from Henslow.

Had his father not objected, Darwin would have accepted the position aboard the *Beagle* then and there. A voyage to South America and around the world was just what he wanted. But his father told him it was a wild scheme. Besides, the life at sea would be a poor influence on a prospective clergyman. Fortunately, his father left one hope, when he added: "If you can find any man of common sense who advises you to go I will give my consent." As good as giving up, Darwin wrote to Henslow, regretfully declining the opportunity. The matter was closed. The next morning Darwin left for the nearby estate of his uncle, Josiah Wedgwood, for some early September hunting.

When his Uncle Josiah heard of the offer, he advised Darwin to go. According to Darwin, his father had always considered Uncle Josiah "one of the most sensible men in the world." Here was Darwin's chance. On August 31 Darwin's uncle drafted a long letter to his father, arguing point by point in Charles' favor. About the trip's not being a suitable preparation for the clergy, Josiah tactfully agreed, then added: "But looking upon him as a man of enlarged curiosity, it affords him such an opportunity of seeing men and things as happens to few." He then drove Darwin the thirty miles back to Shrewsbury himself, to carry on the argument.

Two days later Darwin wrote Henslow a brief note. His father had changed his mind. Darwin then made immediate plans to talk with Henslow and Professor Peacock. Before his appointment as naturalist would be final, however, he would have to meet the most important person of all, Captain Robert FitzRoy. They met in London on September 5, just before lunch.

Charles Darwin at the age of thirty-one. From a watercolor
painted in 1840, four years after the *Beagle*'s return.
COURTESY AMERICAN MUSEUM OF NATURAL HISTORY.

FitzRoy was an unusual man, in many ways a prodigy of the sea. Scarcely four years older than Darwin, FitzRoy had graduated from the Royal Naval Academy at fourteen, was commissioned a lieutenant by twenty, and by twenty-four was captain of the *Beagle*. His reputation as an accurate surveyor was unsurpassed, and he was a superb practical seaman. His men considered him strict, but fair. Many from the first expedition had volunteered to serve aboard the *Beagle* during the second voyage. Admiral King was sending his own son Philip with FitzRoy as cabin boy. Even for so young a man, FitzRoy's personality was forceful, and his aristocratic heritage gave him unshakable self-confidence, and some unusual prejudices.

The separate paths that brought Darwin and FitzRoy together were not the least of their differences. Darwin was tall, over six feet, though his broad shoulders had already developed a slight stoop. His face was round, topped with hair a common shade of brown. His blue-gray eyes were wideset under bushy, intense brows, yet his entire manner suggested a quiet good nature. In contrast, FitzRoy was somber. He was shorter than Darwin, slight in build, but fine-featured and darkly handsome.

Darwin characterized FitzRoy on their first meeting as open and kind, although before their meeting FitzRoy had begun to doubt whether he wanted a complete stranger aboard as naturalist. He had even mentioned in one communication to Darwin that he might be taking a friend. FitzRoy must have reappraised Darwin quickly, for he told him that his friend —real or fictitious —had notified him just before their meeting that he would be unable to sail with the *Beagle*.

It was FitzRoy's straightforwardness that Darwin liked most of all. The day of the meeting Darwin wrote his older sister Susan "There is something most extremely attractive in his manners and way of coming straight to the point." They talked about accommodations, meals, and expenses. FitzRoy seemed concerned over Darwin's comfort and offered him every available convenience, including the use of part of his own cabin. A clue to his temperament was apparent when he asked Darwin if he could "bear being told that I [FitzRoy] want the cabin to myself —when I want to be alone? If we treat each other this way, I hope we shall suit; if not, probably we should wish each other at the devil."

At this point there still may have been doubts in FitzRoy's mind. One of his unusual beliefs was in the principles of Johann Kaspar Lavater, which held that a man's character could be judged solely by the features of his face. FitzRoy later admitted that at first sight he thought the shape of Darwin's nose incompatible with the energy and determination required of the *Beagle*'s future naturalist. Despite this, FitzRoy made his decision. As far as he was concerned, Darwin would sail as the *Beagle*'s naturalist.

The Saturday following their first meeting, Darwin and FitzRoy caught the steamer to Plymouth to see the *Beagle*.

2

H. M. S. Beagle

THE *BEAGLE* was one of a small and lightly armed class of ships common in the British Navy. They were sound and seaworthy, but a relatively high superstructure caused them to roll in heavy weather, earning them the sometimes appropriate nickname of coffins. The *Beagle* was one of FitzRoy's few extravagances, however, and he was single-minded about the ship's safety.

Refitting the *Beagle* had begun in July at Devonport, near Plymouth. FitzRoy removed four of the *Beagle*'s ten cannons and had the deck raised, improving the ship's ability to take heavy seas and increasing space below-decks. For better handling, he had the *Beagle* rerigged as a three-masted bark. The hull, found partially rotted, was then replanked, covered by felt and sheathed with ten tons of copper. Lightning rods, a recent innovation, were fixed atop each mast. Darwin first saw the *Beagle* on Sunday, September 12. Barely 100 feet long and 30 feet wide, the ship seemed unbelievably small.

On October 2 Darwin said good-bye to his family and friends at Shrewsbury and left for London to make last-minute preparations. He intended to take a coastal steamer for Plymouth on the sixteenth in anticipation of the *Beagle*'s sailing late in the month. In the midst of his purchases and meetings with members of London's scientific societies, he received word that the *Beagle* would be delayed at least until November 4. He finally left London for Devonport on October 23, arriving the next day.

Even to Darwin's unnautical eye it was apparent that the *Beagle* would not sail on schedule. The decks were still littered, the refitting incomplete, and FitzRoy's orders had not yet arrived from the Admiralty. For both FitzRoy and Darwin there was plenty of work to do, and the remainder of October slipped by with seemingly endless preparations and equally endless round after round of goodbye luncheons and dinners. Each of Darwin's letters home added something to the growing list of things to take —a few more shirts to be made, a pair of walking shoes, a small book on taxidermy left in his bedroom, his new microscope.

FitzRoy's task now was to prepare the *Beagle* for a voyage that would last perhaps four years. He bought the best provisions and equipment possible. Chronometers, the precise timepieces used in determining longitude, were essential. FitzRoy bought twenty-four of them; then for good measure he hired a skilled instrument maker at his own expense to maintain them. He also commissioned Augustus Earle, an artist, to sketch views of coastlines and harbors. Nearly 400 pounds sterling, an enormous sum then, was spent on firearms, which FitzRoy valued equally for self-protection and obtaining fresh meat. He advised Darwin to buy an expensive brace of pistols and never to venture ashore without them.

Darwin found that the *Beagle* would carry nearly seventy crewmen, including a doctor, a carpenter, a small detachment of Marines, as well as the three Indians FitzRoy was returning to Tierra del Fuego. Everyone was cramped for space. Darwin's quarters turned out to be not part of the captain's cabin, but a small space at the end of the drawing table in the ship's chart room, far at the stern. He shared the chart room with a young lieutenant named Stokes. His plant and animal collection would be stored in a small area beneath the forecastle. In a letter to Henslow he wrote, "The absolute want of room is an evil that nothing can surmount."

Darwin prepared for the voyage much like the typical naturalist of the time. A naturalist in the 1830's was expected to be equally at home with geologist's hammer and compass or botanist's microscope. The biological sciences that we know —botany, zoology, biology, and ecology —were not as clearly defined and specialized as today. FitzRoy wanted Darwin to pay particular attention to the recognition of precious minerals, which fit well with Darwin's new liking for geology. But he also planned to collect plants and animals, particularly the invertebrates, and make descriptions of any scientific phenomena which struck his fancy.

His intended preoccupation with collecting and describing of phenomena was also in keeping with the scientific philosophy of the time. The explanation of *why* phenomena occur was definitely not the scientist's main task. John Herschel's influential book *Preliminary Discourse on the Study of Natural Philosophy,* which Darwin had read and admired at Cambridge, stated that scientific inquiry should be of a limited nature, concerned with how things happen, not why, and, most important, that science should be consistent with religious truth.

For the scientist of the early nineteenth century, the mingling of science with theology shaped his thoughts more than anything else. Much of the science of Darwin's time, true to Herschel's principles, involved a search to support the literal interpretation of the Old Testament. As Herschel warned, scientists should not concern themselves with the origin of anything—rocks, plants, animals, or whatever—but rather with their action or how they function. The origin or cause of phenomena, according to the theologians, was thought to be an all-powerful, designing Creator. The most minute phenomena could be traced back ultimately to some divine plan, even so trivial an occurrence as the snatching of a gnat in midflight by a hungry frog.

As it would later confront Darwin, the popular view of the origin of species was derived from the same kind of thinking. Species of plants and animals were thought to have been devised in their present form and put in their present environments on earth by the design of the

Creator. Moreover, the species were fixed and unchangeable, "immutable," in the scientific phraseology of the time. There was occasional scientific discussion about the idea that present species may have evolved from earlier life. What was lacking was not the idea of evolution, but enough conclusive evidence to show that it existed. The whole idea of evolution could be applied to Sedgwick's comment to Darwin regarding the shell found in the quarry: if it were found to be so, much of the scientific thinking that had gone before would be invalid.

Despite the wide belief in the immutability of species, the idea of evolution was not new. Darwin's own grandfather, Erasmus, had written a book in 1794 titled *Zoonomia*. It was intended to be a medical textbook, but it included a discussion of the idea of the descent of species by evolution. *Zoonomia* was widely read in scientific circles, translated into several languages, and was probably discussed in the Darwin household. Years later Darwin read *Zoonomia* again, noting that Erasmus Darwin's theory, like so many of the scientific works of the time, was woefully short of facts to document his speculation.

One of the most discussed books on evolution was written in 1809, the year Darwin was born, by a Frenchman, Jean Baptiste Lamarck. The main shortcoming of Lamarck's work was his explanation of how evolution could occur. Lamarck's idea was that animals evolved slowly by an unconscious physical striving to adjust better to a particular physical environment. Thus, one generation would change its physical characteristics slightly, passing on the changes to the next generation. Both

Erasmus Darwin and Lamarck believed in the erroneous idea that characteristics acquired during an organism's lifetime were passed on to the following generation. In this manner, hypothesized Lamarck, the giraffe became a long-necked creature, admirably suited for gnawing the tender leaves from the high branches of trees in the African selva after generations of unconscious striving.

Lamarck was poorly translated into English, however, and he was often interpreted incorrectly. The majority of naturalists in England believed Lamarck thought that animals consciously willed themselves to change. Consequently, the theory of the "French atheist," as he was called in England, was never taken seriously.

Darwin may have discussed the idea of evolution at Edinburgh and read an occasional scientific paper on the subject, for he was an avid reader. Still, the idea of evolution rang of heresy. As Darwin prepared for the voyage, in all likelihood he agreed with the scientific philosophy of his teachers, the majority of scientists of the day, and the loudly proclaimed orthodoxy of FitzRoy. Before the end of the voyage, however, Darwin's unrelenting curiosity and his ability to see things as they were, not as they were supposed to be, would lead him in his own direction.

By early November the *Beagle*'s refitting was complete, as were most of Darwin's preparations for the voyage. Still the orders to sail had not arrived from the Admiralty, and the waiting to get under way became nearly unbearable for Darwin. Finally, on November 15, 1831, he wrote Henslow:

The orders are come down from the Admiralty, and everything is finally settled. We positively sail the last day of this month, and I think before that time the vessel will be ready. She looks most beautiful, even a landsman must admire her. *We* all think her the most perfect vessel ever turned out of the Dockyard. One thing is certain, no vessel has been fitted out so expensively, and with so much care. Everything that can be made so is of mahogany, and nothing can exceed the neatness and beauty of all the accommodations. The instructions are very general, and leave a great deal to the Captain's discretion and judgment. . . .

Added to FitzRoy's orders was a lengthy memorandum from the Admiralty to FitzRoy that the coasts between the mouth of the Plata River and Tierra del Fuego and northward on the Pacific coast to Valparaiso were very poorly surveyed, the only charts based on the early, inaccurate ones of the Spanish. Wrote Beaufort:

Of this kind of half-knowledge we have had too much: the present state of science, which affords such ample means, seems to demand that whatever is now done should be finally done; and that coasts, which are constantly visited by English vessels, should no longer have the motley appearance of alternate error and accuracy. . . .

FitzRoy's work was clear: to finish once and for all the survey of South America's southern coasts, a staggering task for a twenty-seven-year-old captain and one small ship.

On Monday, November 21, Darwin noted in his pocket notebook: "Carried all my books and instruments on board the *Beagle.*" The brief phrases that he penciled into the notebook would be enlarged later as passages in the diary he had begun his first day at Devonport. By the end of the voyage there would be eighteen pocket notebooks filled with short comments on everything from the weather to the characteristics of his sailing mates. The diary written from the notebooks would reach more than 800 pages.

On November 23 he wrote:

This has been a very important day in the annals of the *Beagle*; at one o'clock she loosed from the moorings & sailed about a mile to Barnett pool. Here she will remain till the day of sailing arrives. This little sail was to me very interesting, everything so new & different to what one has ever seen, the Coxwain's piping, the manning the yards, the men working at the hawsers to the sound of the fife; but nothing is so striking as the rapidity & decision of the orders & the alertness with which they are obeyed. There remains very little to be done to make ready for sailing. All the stores are completed & yesterday between 5 & 6 thousands canisters of preserved meat were stowed away. Not one inch of room is lost, the hold would scarcely contain another bag of bread. My notions of the inside of a ship were almost as definite as those of some men of a man . . . a large cavity containing water & bread mingled in hopeless confusion.

But it was more than a month before the *Beagle* was able to leave, and the delay left Darwin depressed and restless to begin. He even began to suspect that his father's objections were right all along. Doubts were on him — doubt about leaving his old friends and family behind for so many years; doubt about his ability to get along at sea;

and, finally, doubt about his talent as a naturalist. Only the voyage itself would put an end to his doubts. Finally, three days before the year 1831 ended, the *Beagle* sailed from England, bound via the Canary Islands for the coast of Brazil.

3

To Green Brazil
DECEMBER, 1831–MARCH, 1832

OUT OF Devonport in the open sea, Fitz-Roy set the *Beagle*'s course south toward the blue-green waters of the equator. Winter had a tight grip on the Bay of Biscay, and the first week of sailing was rough and stormy. Darwin was seasick almost before they had passed Devonport Light. Appropriate as the chart room may have been as a study, its location far at the *Beagle*'s stern made it rise and fall like an elevator with each pitch of the *Beagle* through the stormy seas. Darwin spent most of the week in his hammock, a book in his hand to distract his mind from his stomach. He was occasionally able to force down a few raisins, but once, when he tried to get out of the hammock, he nearly fainted from weakness. No one who hasn't suffered seasickness, he noted in his diary, could fully imagine its horrors.

Then the weather eased, the gray of northern waters and weather giving way to predominate blue. Under clear skies and with a smooth sea, Darwin began putting his new way of life in order, his letters and comments in his diary reflecting his enthusiasm. In one letter to his father, he wrote, "If it was not for sea-sickness the whole world would be sailors." In a later letter to his sister Susan, he described the routine of a typical day:

I do not think I have ever given you an account of how the day passes. We breakfast at eight o'clock. The invariable maxim is to throw away all politeness — that is, never to wait for each other, and bolt off the minute one has done eating, &c. At sea, when the weather is calm, I work at marine animals, with which the whole ocean abounds. If there is any sea up I am either sick or contrive to read some voyage or travels. At one we dine. You shore-going people are lamentably mistaken about the manner of living on board. We have never yet (nor shall we) dined off salt meat. Rice and peas and *calavanses* are excellent vegetables, and, with good bread, who could want more? . . . At five we have tea. The midshipmen's berth have all their meals an hour before us, and the gun-room an hour afterwards.

By January 5 they had sighted the fabled peak of Tenerife, the island so romantically described by Humboldt. But Darwin's growing excitement to follow Humboldt's footsteps exploring the island was cut short by the British vice-consul, as he drew alongside the *Beagle* in a small boat. Fear of epidemics carried from England presented FitzRoy with a dilemma. Darwin describes what happened in a letter to Henslow:

Till arriving at Teneriffe (we did not touch at Madeira) I was scarcely out of my hammock, and really suffered more than you can well imagine from such a cause. At Santa Cruz, whilst looking amongst the clouds for the Peak, and repeating to myself Humboldt's sublime descriptions, it was announced we must perform twelve days' strict quarantine. We had made a short passage, so "Up jib," and away for St. Jago. You will say all this sounds very bad, and so it was; but from that to the present time it has been nearly one scene of continual enjoyment. A net over the stern kept me at full work till we arrived at St. Jago. . . .

One great source of perplexity to me is an utter ignorance whether I note the right facts, and whether they are of sufficient importance to interest others. In the one thing collecting I cannot go wrong. . . . I took several specimens of an Octopus which possessed a most marvellous power of changing its colours, equalling any chameleon, and evidently accommodating the changes to the colour of the ground which it passed over. Yellowish green, dark brown, and red, were the prevailing colours; this fact appears to be new, as far as I can find out. . . .

. . . I find my life on board when we are on blue water most delightful, so very comfortable and quiet—it is almost impossible to be idle, and that for me is saying a good deal. . . .

The *Beagle* spent three weeks at the Cape Verde Islands, and it was in port where Darwin's work began in earnest. At each port of call Darwin planned as many brief excursions as time would permit to collect specimens of plants and animals, study the geology, and describe what he saw. When the *Beagle* undertook more lengthy surveys along the coast, he would take longer trips into the countryside, catching up with the *Beagle* at predetermined places. Between stints ashore, as the *Beagle* made longer reaches along the coast, Darwin would work aboard, writing out the sketches from his pocket notebooks at length for his diary and analyzing and packing his collections for periodic shipment back to England. The diary was Darwin's prize, and he considered it not entirely a scientific document but "one long letter" to his friends and family about the voyage.

Leaving the Cape Verde Islands, the *Beagle* continued its southern course. To Darwin's surprise the *Beagle* began to feel like home, and his small working space turned out more a blessing than a curse. On February 8 he wrote to his father, "A ship is singularly comfortable for all sorts of work. Everything is so close at hand, and being cramped makes one so methodical, that in the end I have been a gainer."

By February 16 the *Beagle* had reached St. Paul Rocks, a little group of pinnacles "peeping up in the midst of the Atlantic." FitzRoy made some sightings to double-check the calculations made during the first expedition. Wrote Darwin:

There was such a scene here. Wickham (1st Lieutenant) and I were the only two who landed with guns and geological hammers, &c. The birds by myriads were too close to shoot; we then tried stones, but at last . . . my geological hammer was the instrument of death. We soon loaded the boat with birds and eggs. Whilst we were so engaged, the men in the boat were fairly fighting with the sharks for such magnificent fish as you could not see in the London market. . . .

Life at sea for the new sailor had its shortcomings

Neptune's constables welcoming all hands crossing the equator for the first time, Darwin included. A drawing by the *Beagle*'s artist, Augustus Earle.

beyond seasickness, however. The day following the visit to St. Paul Rocks the *Beagle* crossed the line, the constellations of the Northern Hemisphere disappearing one by one below the horizon. Crossing the equator for the first time, Darwin was among the initiates presided over by Neptune's Constables. In the melee that followed, Darwin ended up with his face rubbed with paint and tar, then shaved with "a saw that represents the razor." The general dousing with salt water that followed was so spirited that even FitzRoy, who considered such rites only as necessary diversion for a restless crew, was left soaked to the skin.

Less eventful was the *Beagle*'s landing at Fernando de Noronha, an island off the easternmost point of South America, then sailing southwest once more. Near Cabo Saño Roque, Darwin sighted the rich, historic northeast coast of Brazil.

Brazil was quite a different country from the others sharing the South American continent. By size alone it would have been unique. Although its western boundaries were ill defined, even by the roughest measures, Brazil occupied half the continent. With a population estimated at over 4,000,000, there were more Brazilians in South America than in the rest of the countries combined. The uniqueness of Brazil resulted from its settlement by the Portuguese, not the Spanish, and from the vast expanse of its land which lay within the tropics.

Colonization by Portugal alone was enough to send Brazil's history in a different direction. Even before South America's discovery, a unique agreement had dealt Brazil to the Portuguese Empire. In the last decades of the

1400's Spain and Portugal were competing for colonies in spice-rich Asia. Portugal, though smaller and poorer than Spain, fronted on the sea and had managed to pioneer the route to Asia around the southern tip of Africa. The Spanish struck west. Two years after Columbus' discovery in the Caribbean, Spain and Portugal drew up the Treaty of Tordesillas, which in general divided the undiscovered lands of the New World between them. The treaty called for a line of separation slightly west of Africa. Lands to the west would be Spanish. Those to the east, including the undiscovered bulge of South America later to become Brazil, would go to Portugal. While Spain continued its explorations of the Spanish Indies, Portugal launched more voyages around Africa, eventually establishing colonies in Ceylon, India, and Angola. On one such voyage in 1502 the Portuguese explorer Pedro Alvares Cabral stumbled on the eastern coast of South America after being blown off course by storm winds. He claimed the new land for Portugal and, after exploring a week, continued his voyage to India.

Amerigo Vespucci explored more of the coast two years later, adding in his reports that it appeared to be a land of cannibals and parrots. For nearly a half century following Cabral's discovery, Portugal chose to do little with its newfound territory. In 1532 the king divided 4,000 miles of Brazilian coast into twelve districts and handed out each to favorites of the Crown with a vague hope of colonization. A few settlers landed and succeeded in earning a meager existence, despite Portugal's indifference, French raiders, and Indian attacks.

While Spanish conquistadors conquered the Incas high

on the Andean plateaus and funneled a wealth of gold and silver back to Spain, the Portuguese settlers exported only a few shipments of a dyewood called *pau brasil,* which earned little more for the new land than its name. In those first years of colonization Brazil was a speculation, the spices and silks of Asia a sure thing.

The history of Brazil began with sugar. In 1532 a halfhearted attempt to introduce sugar from the Cape Verde Islands was made along the northeast coast. The first successful venture came a few years later. In 1549 the King of Portugal felt the colony finally needed a governor-general. That year his appointee, Tomé de Souza, landed at a broad, crescent-shaped bay situated in the district named Bahia. His six ships brought 300 functionaries paid by the king, 400 assorted renegades banished from Portugal, 300 colonists from the wealthy north of Portugal, and an assortment of missionaries, engineers, and soldiers. Sugar was introduced soon after. Brazil had its first capital and the beginnings of a thriving colony.

Following nearly the same course as Cabral did, the *Beagle* made its way leisurely toward the port of Salvador, in Bahia, the sight of Tomé de Souza's first colony, charting the shoals and reefs that lined the coast. Unlike the west coast of South America, which is dominated by the massive presence of the Andes, the east coast is low, meeting the sea with sharp cliffs backed by rolling hills or plateaus.

From Cabo São Roque south, much of the Brazilian coast was then covered by a margin of tropical forest which the Indians called *mata.* Modern botanists classify *mata* more formally as tropical semideciduous forest. As far inland from the coast as moist winds penetrate, often 50 or 60 miles, trees of mahogany, elm, and *jacarandá* grew, mixed with wild pineapples, ferns, and mosses. These forests are slightly less dense than the true jungle or evergreen rain forests that line the Amazon and its tributaries. Both are a product of year-round warm temperatures and abundant rainfall.

By early morning on February 28, the *Beagle* was close enough to the coast for Darwin to see the tropical forests, etched bright green against the brilliant blue sky of a tropical day. By eleven in the morning the *Beagle* had sailed into the crescent-shaped bay with the city of Salvador at its northern edge. "It would be difficult [to] imagine . . ." Darwin wrote in his diary, "anything so magnificent." It was all Darwin could do to contain his excitement until the next day, when he could get off the *Beagle* and plunge into the work he longed for. The following night he wrote in his diary:

The day has passed delightfully: delight is however a weak term for such transports of pleasure: I have been wandering by myself in a Brazilian forest: . . . the elegance of the grasses, the novelty of the parasitical plants, the beauty of the flowers. . . . To a person fond of Natural history such a day as this brings with it pleasure more acute than he ever may again experience.

During the three months Darwin stayed in Brazil, he never ceased to tire of wandering through the tropical forests and attempting to describe them. The diversity of plant species —hundreds per acre —and the innumerable kinds of insect life left him at a loss in trying to describe them. No one, not even Humboldt, could capture the reality of the tropics. Much of the first week at Salvador Darwin spent gathering specimens in the tropical forests, which were found everywhere beyond the city's confines. He made the beginnings of his collections of tropical insects and flowers, his studies of geology taking second place to what the forests could offer. On March 5, after an especially exciting day of working and shooting with young King, Darwin confided in his diary what a joy it was to have as a duty "what has for some years given me so much pleasure."

By the next day, however, a scratch on his knee had swollen badly. The next week he spent aboard the *Beagle,* either grumbling in his hammock or lying quietly on deck. It was on March 12, while still confined, aboard the *Beagle,* that he made the first references in his diary to slavery.

At the time there was tremendous agitation in England, especially by the Whig Party, to outlaw slavery. The shipping of slaves had been outlawed in 1810, yet as of 1832 no European nation had abolished slavery.

Darwin shared a dislike of slavery with many Englishmen, although slavery itself was little practiced in England and his knowledge of it was largely secondhand. Since abolishing the slave trade, England had begun using its naval might to force other nations to cease trading in slaves also. For the tropical countries whose plantations depended on slaves, the bullying by the British was unpopular, and whenever possible it was ignored. The 1826 commercial treaty between England

A portrayal of the tropical forest of Brazil by the German artist Maurice Rugendas. Rugendas traveled through much of the continent a decade before Darwin's arrival, sketching the people and the land as he went. Darwin admired this particular rendering immensely. COURTESY NATIONAL ARCHIVES, RIO DE JANEIRO.

and Brazil contained a clause which, if followed, would have meant the eventual end of slavery in Brazil. But the plantation owners held the power in the government, and the letter of the law was ignored. As Darwin observed, slaves and slavery were everywhere along coastal Brazil. The dependence on slavery had been with the Brazilians from the very first, developing as far and wide as the plantations for which Brazil was famous.

The first colonists had come to Brazil to make money, and sugar raising in the warm tropical environment seemed to provide the best opportunity. More than a fertile soil and warm climate, profitable sugar raising needed cheap labor and an investment in land and machinery. Many colonists on the northeast coast, aristocrats from the rich north of Portugal, were used to managing the work of others and were financially able to invest in land and machinery. Like their Spanish neighbors on the Iberian Peninsula, they brought to South America a love for large estates and the elegant way of life these could provide for them. They also brought the habit of slavery. The Moors, who had occupied Portugal until the mid 1300's, came from Africa and brought a long history of slavery to the Portuguese, as well as a tradition of tolerance toward cultures different from their own. The Portuguese inherited both of these traditions from the Moors and introduced them eventually to Brazil.

As a source of slaves the colonists first tried the Indians. At the time of discovery, the Indian population of Brazil may have numbered 800,000. They were more primitive than the tribes of the Inca Empire, mainly numerous isolated groups that lived by fishing and hunting. They were unsuited by temperament or tradition to field work in the tropical sun, but to the colonists they proved better than nothing. As the sugar estates, called *fazendas,* spread along the fertile plain inland from Salvador and into the *mata* along the coast, the demand for Indian slaves increased. To the south of the sugar coast, roving bands of pioneers called *bandeirantes,* or flag carriers, made a brisk business selling captured Indians while they explored the interior for gold and precious stones. Still, it was not enough. A continuing demand for slaves, combined with a loss of many Indians by famine and disease, made Indian slavery too expensive. Early in Brazil's history, slave traders from Africa found a growing market for their wares: Negroes from Angola, Dahomey, and the Sudan. By 1585 there were 10,000 African slaves in the Pernambuco district —three times the number of whites —and 3,000 to 4,000 slaves in Bahia.

By the end of the 1500's the sugar *fazenda,* worked by Negro slaves, had become the most significant aspect of Brazilian life. Each *fazenda* was almost a small colony, as independent as it could make itself. Each had its huge stone house, or *casa grande,* which was not only the residence of the *fazendeiro* but also the hospital, school, bank, and guest quarters. Some *fazendas* were large enough to accommodate 100 guests. The furnishings were most likely from Europe. Beneath the floor of the attached chapel the *fazendeiro*'s family was buried. Funerals, as well as the education of his children, were administered by the *fazenda*'s own priest. Moreover, each *casa grande* had a retinue of servants and shoemakers, ironwrights and carpenters. Nearby gardens of fruits and vegetables fed family and slaves alike.

The increasing taste in Europe for sugar, a commodity once so rare it was sold in small parcels by apothecaries, made the northeast of Brazil rich.

But the entire history of Brazil has been a story of boom and bust in one region after another. The end of Brazil's first great boom was caused by an unusual combination of circumstances. During the 1600's the Dutch, then at the height of their power, invaded part of the northeast coast to exploit the success of sugar. By the time they were driven out, thirty years later, they had learned the techniques of sugar raising. The Dutch founded plantations in the Caribbean, much closer to the important markets in Europe. Then near the headwaters of the Rio São Francisco, hundreds of miles south of the sugar areas, a party of *bandeirantes* struck gold in 1692. A new boom had begun. Adventurers from every part of Brazil flocked to the gold country. Mining camps sprouted in the wilderness, and the fort of Rio de Janeiro, 1,000 miles south of Salvador, grew into a sprawling city overnight as the terminal of mule trains to the gold country. In 1763 the capital was shifted from Salvador to Rio. The sugar boom had ended, and the northeast never recovered.

By the time Darwin visited Brazil, mining, like sugar, had suffered its decline. A new boom was in its infancy. Coffee had been introduced from French Guiana in 1723 and had been grown in small quantities since then. By 1770 it was cultivated near Rio, where small

A small part of Rio's gigantic slave market. COURTESY
NATIONAL ARCHIVES, RIO DE JANEIRO.

patches of *mata* had been cleared to expose the red soil in which coffee thrived.

During the early 1800's coffee growing had spread to the Paraíba Valley inland from Rio, a natural pathway to the hilly forested uplands near São Paulo. There coffee proved to be Brazil's most prosperous boom, and by the 1830's the coffee *fazendeiro* was already taking his place in Brazil's land-loving aristocracy. Like the sugar plantations, the coffee *fazendas* demanded large amounts of slave labor.

Between the end of the 1500's and the abolition of the slave trade in 1856 the Negro was the largest group coming to Brazil, numbering in Darwin's time perhaps 800,000. Slavery in Brazil was one of Darwin's bitterest memories. Mention of it in his diary he later called an explosion of feelings. References to that "curse of Christian nations" crept into some of his letters. And seeing slavery firsthand seemed to dull some of the glitter of the tropical landscape. In a letter to a former Cambridge schoolmate, John Herbert, he wrote:

I was not previously aware how intimately what may be called the moral part is connected with the enjoyment of scenery. . . . Change the English labourer into a poor slave, working for another, and you will hardly recognise the same view. . . .

As strongly opposed as he was to slavery, he did admit, at least early in his visit to Brazil, that "the greater part of the slave population is far happier than one would be . . . inclined to believe." Slavery in Brazil was probably less harsh than in Spanish South America or, for that matter, in the United States at the time. A slave had certain rights. Under the law he was treated as an individual instead of as property. A slave could own land, work a few days each week for himself, and with a permissive master even purchase his own freedom. And by the time of Darwin's visit, the Negro had made more significant contributions in Brazil than in any other South American country. Many slaves had come from the Sudan, a region of Africa with a long history of technological innovation, including iron smelting. They learned trades quickly, and many slaves and free Negroes operated Brazil's sugar mills and mine smelters.

The Moorish idea of tolerance, moreover, left the Portuguese in Brazil with few taboos against absorbing different elements of culture into their own. The Portuguese Darwin heard spoken in Salvador was sprinkled with African words and was more melodious than that spoken in Portugal. The rich foods tasted of *dende,* the savory oil favored by the slaves for cooking. The slaves, in turn, had borrowed elements of the Catholic religion from their masters and mixed them with their own more primitive rites brought from Africa. During his first two weeks in Salvador, Darwin saw the pre-Easter religious festival Carnaval. The samba he saw danced on its cobbled streets to the rhythm of drums, sticks or anything that would rattle had its roots in the *batuque,* brought from the rain forests of West Africa. At all levels of society, except the highest, the Brazilians mixed regardless of racial origin. Even then, most people failed to recognize that their contributions to a culture, and racial mixture were already producing something neither African, Indian, or Portuguese, but uniquely Brazilian.

Despite the deep and lasting impression made by the Negroes as a group, the lot of the individual slave was subject to the kindness or brutality of his master, a fact that became apparent very quickly to Darwin. An argument with FitzRoy over the treatment of slaves very nearly ended his part in the voyage when it had scarcely begun.

Considering FitzRoy's temperament, his political opposition to Darwin, and his penchant for working himself to exhaustion, the small cabin where they dined nightly was a potential battleground from the beginning. Their first clash occurred one night at dinner and was described later by Darwin in his autobiography. Of FitzRoy he wrote:

. . . he defended and praised slavery, which I abominated, and told me that he had just visited a great slave-owner, who had called up many of his slaves and asked them whether they were happy, and whether they wished to be free, and all answered "No." I then asked him, perhaps with a sneer, whether he thought that the answer of slaves in the presence of their master was worth anything?

With that FitzRoy flew into a rage. Since Darwin had doubted his word, their arrangment would come to an end then and there. The news spread around the ship that the captain and the flycatcher had argued. After tempers cooled, a peace was mediated by the crew, an apology passing from FitzRoy to Darwin a few hours later.

With both his knee and his friendship with FitzRoy

mended, Darwin spent the final week in Salvador much like the first —collecting insects, tropical plants, and whenever possible studying a little geology. On March 17 he and Philip King took a final stroll ashore. It was a bright, clear evening, the gentle sea breeze absent for once, leaving the night silent and for Darwin somewhat memorable. He noted in his diary: "nothing could be better adapted for fixing in the mind the last & glorious remembrance of Bahia." On the morning of the next day the *Beagle* weighed anchor and, fighting strong currents but with a light wind, slowly left Salvador behind.

4

The Capital of Brazil
APRIL, 1832–JULY, 1832

IT TOOK more than two weeks for the *Beagle* to sail the 1,000 miles between Salvador and Rio de Janeiro. The trip was smooth, the sea unruffled, and the sky cloudless and bright blue. Darwin enjoyed this kind of sailing immensely, not once suffering the woes of seasickness. He fished and one day caught a shark. He walked the *Beagle*'s small deck, marveling at the order of life at sea. He read, added notes to his diary, and got to know better his shipmates, who would be his friends for some years to come. By April 3 the sight of Cabo Frio signaled their closeness to Rio and to the newspapers and letters from home that surely awaited them. The next day the *Beagle* entered magnificent Guanabara Bay and, near the quays of Brazil's capital, anchored next to a British

Another Rugendas drawing. Rio with magnificent Guanabara Bay beyond. COURTESY NATIONAL ARCHIVES, RIO DE JANEIRO.

flagship, home for the commander of the South America station, to whom FitzRoy would report.

The ship's artist, Augustus Earle, had lived in Brazil before joining the *Beagle,* and the next day he guided Darwin through the narrow, crowded streets of the largest city in South America. By the time of the *Beagle*'s visit, Rio's population was nearly 200,000, four times as many as in Buenos Aires, far south in Argentina, and twice as many as in Salvador.

The city was founded in 1567, when in order to protect Portugal's claim to the long stretch of unpopulated coast between Salvador and São Vicente against French intrusion, the fort and a small church were built and christened São Sebastião de Rio de Janeiro. The site was one of the most beautiful imaginable, the huge natural harbor of Guanabara Bay surrounded by jagged, green-clad mountains and dotted with bald granite domes.

If Guanabara Bay had been situated at the edge of a fertile plain like the Pampas, it would have been a prize. But behind the narrow, flat coastal strip, a steep escarpment rises abruptly several thousand feet, an imposing rock wall that would forever make access to the interior difficult. Until the gold strike in Minas Gerais in 1694, there was no reason even to attempt to link Rio with the rolling hills that lay behind the escarpment. Guanabara Bay was a magnificent door to an empty room, the interior unpopulated except for the forays of *bandeirantes.*

Gold justified building trails that zigzagged down the rocky face of the escarpment, and along them mules brought bars of gold 300 miles from Minas Gerais to the safety of Rio and returned with colonists, slaves and supplies for the growing population inland. When enough people had moved to Rio and to the gold country to shift Brazil's center of wealth and population away from the northeast coast, the busy seaport was made capital of Brazil in 1763.

The arrival of the Portuguese royal family in 1808 ultimately gave Rio the character Darwin saw. The Portuguese ships, escorted by a British fleet, followed by the stepping ashore of the ruling Braganza family with their entourage, including army generals, officials, courtiers, and exiled aristocrats —10,000 people in all—must have been a curious spectacle for the *fazendeiros,* their slaves and Rio's shopkeepers.

The court was equally surprised. Rio was already a city of 130,000 people, and the streets were laid out orderly enough in a neat rectangular pattern. Still, Rio was without waterworks, sewers, newspapers, or theaters; its docks were ramshackle, and the houses, neat and whitewashed, had not a window pane among them. Rio was a strange combination of tropical charm and indescribable filth.

During the twelve years that Rio was capital of the Portuguese Empire, the city benefited immensely. The year following the Crown's arrival, Prince Regent Dom João, ruling for his insane mother, Queen Maria I, threw open Brazil to trade with the world. Waiting expectantly were the British. In came British trade goods and investments. During the 1800's Brazil received more British investments than any other South American country. As Darwin observed, Rio was the commercial capital of South America. Dom João's reign also brought Rio's first newspaper, a military school, a new hospital, a royal library, and botanical gardens, which Darwin later visited. The endless court functions enlivened the city's cultural life. Following independence, an overhead aqueduct was constructed to carry water to public fountains. It's arched supports became one of the prominent pieces of Rio's architecture.

But the location of government in Rio had its ill effects. Many people who arrived with the royal family found little to do, and most eventually became minor government officials. The size of the government swelled beyond necessity. With it grew complicated procedures and ornate governmental rituals, which from that time forward became almost a Brazilian way of life. Darwin soon ran afoul of it.

The day following the *Beagle*'s arrival in Rio, Darwin met an Englishman, Patrick Lennon. Lennon had come to Brazil twenty years before with the first of the British traders, subsequently making a fortune selling spectacles and thermometers. He owned a large estate 100 miles north of Rio, which he visited every few months. He invited Darwin to join him on the next visit, a few days hence.

It was an unexpected opportunity. Lennon told him the trip would be through sparsely populated land, much of it covered by tropical forest. He would have to obtain a passport from the government to visit the interior and do some hurried packing. In the mind of the young Englishman Darwin, used to precision and order and direct in his manner of dealing with people, obtaining a passport seemed a simple thing. The whole process, however, turned out to be a vexing confusion of what appeared to

One of the crowded main streets of Rio, appearing much
as it must have during Darwin's visit ashore. COURTESY
NATIONAL ARCHIVES, RIO DE JANEIRO.

be useless and intricate procedures. On April 6 he wrote
in his diary:

The day has been frittered away in obtaining the passports
for my expedition into the interior. It is never very pleasant to
submit to the insolence of men in office; but to the Brazilians,
who are as contemptible in their minds as their persons are
miserable, it is nearly intolerable. But the prospects of wild
forests . . . will make any Naturalist lick the dust even from the
foot of a Brazillian.

The party left April 8. In addition to Lennon, his
nephew, and Darwin, there was a Mr. Laurie, whom
Darwin described as a clever, selfish, unprincipled Scotsman, half slave merchant, half swindler. There were also
a friend of Laurie's named Gosling, one slave, and a guide.
Darwin noted in his diary that the wilds of Brazil had
probably never seen a more extraordinary set of adventures. They left in midmorning, the day already hot, the
woods they passed through still except for the lazy flutter-
ing of large, brightly colored butterflies. They were to
follow the narrow coastal plain east from Rio through
alternate marshes and dense forests to Cabo Frio, then
turn north to the Rio Macaé, following the river inland
to Lennon's *fazenda*. By late morning they had passed
through the last of the cultivated land and into tropical
forest penetrated only by gleams of sunlight. Darwin com-
mented that the grandeur of the forest could not be exceeded. The trees wound with lianas and clinging orchids
reminded him of the engravings he had admired of the
German artist Maurice Rugendas. "I was at an utter loss
how . . . to admire this scene." At midday they arrived

at the small village of Ithacaia and sat out the heat of the day there. But even here the marks of slavery were noted by Darwin:

As the moon rose early, we determined to start the same evening for our sleeping-place at the Lagoa Marcia. As it was growing dark we passed under one of the massive, bare, and steep hills of granite which are so common in this country. This spot is notorious from having been, for a long time, the residence of some runaway slaves, who, by cultivating a little ground near the top, contrived to eke out a subsistence. At length, they were . . . seized with the exception of one old woman, who, sooner than again be led into slavery, dashed herself to pieces from the summit of the mountain. In a Roman matron this would have been called the noble love of freedom: in a poor negress it is mere brutal obstinacy.

After spending a miserable night within range of the "distant and sullen roar of the sea" and a day following a narrow road that ran between the ocean and salt lagoons to the interior, Darwin and his party stopped at a *venda*, the Portuguese name for an inn in those days.

As the vênda here was a very good one, and I have the pleasant, but rare remembrance, of an excellent dinner, I will be grateful and presently describe it, as the type of its class. These houses are often large, and are built of thick upright posts, with boughs interwoven, and afterwards plastered. They seldom have floors, and never glazed windows; but are generally pretty well roofed. Universally the front part is open, forming a kind of verandah, in which tables and benches are placed. The bedrooms join on each side, and here the passenger may sleep as comfortably as he can, on a wooden platform, covered by a thin straw mat. The vênda stands in a courtyard, where the horses are fed. On first arriving, it was our custom to unsaddle the horses and give them their Indian corn; then, with a low bow, to ask the senhór to do us the favour to give us something to eat. "Any thing you choose, sir," was his usual answer. For the first few times, vainly I thanked providence for having guided us to so good a man. The conversation proceeding, the case universally became deplorable.

"Any fish can you do us the favour of giving?"

"Oh! no, sir."

"Any soup?"

"No, sir."

"Any bread?"

"Oh! no, sir."

"Any dried meat?"

"Oh! no, sir."

If we were lucky, by waiting a couple of hours, we obtained fowls, rice and farinha. It not unfrequently happened, that we were obliged to kill, with stones, the poultry for our own supper. When thoroughly exhausted by fatigue and hunger, we timorously hinted that we should be glad of our meal, the pompous and (though true) most unsatisfactory answer was, "It will be ready when it is ready."

By the third day they reached the *fazenda* of a Senhor Figuireda and remained there several days. It was a typical coffee *fazenda* near the northern limit of the coffee-growing region. The house was simple, wrote Darwin in his diary, but well suited to the climate. The richness of the land particularly impressed him. Beans, manioc, and rice, the principal starch plants of the diet, grew in abundance. A large stock of cattle grazed nearby, and the woods were full of game. The country's prosperity was reflected at the evening meals, where, "if the table did not groan, the guests surely did."

Though bothered as he was by slavery, Darwin began to sense what life was like on a *fazenda*. The way of life of the *fazendeiro* differed as much from that of shopkeepers and bureaucrats of Rio as did the quietness and beauty of the countryside from the noise and squalor of the city:

As long as the idea of slavery could be banished, there was something exceedingly fascinating in the simple and patriarchal style of living: it was such a perfect retirement and independence from the rest of the world . . . On such *fazendas* as these, I have no doubt the slaves pass happy and contented lives. On Saturday and Sunday they work for themselves, and in this fertile climate the labour of two days is sufficient to support a man and his family for the whole week.

Having reached Lennon's *fazenda*, they remained several days. While Lennon made his usual periodic inspection, Darwin roamed the tropical forest that existed everywhere beyond cleared land. Later he wrote Henslow:

Here I first saw a tropical forest in all its sublime grandeur — nothing but the reality can give any idea how wonderful, how magnificent the scene is. . . . I formerly admired Humboldt, I now almost adore him; he alone gives any notion of the feelings . . . on first entering the Tropics. . . .

Returning to Rio, they followed nearly the same route.

Then, at the village of Madre de Deus, they turned onto what was supposed to be a major road leading to Rio de Janeiro. It was in such a bad state that Darwin noted no wheeled carriages except bullock-drawn wagons could pass along it. Along the road he saw an occasional wooden cross, "to signify where human blood has been spilled."

By the evening of April 23 they were back in Rio. During the three weeks, Darwin had ridden more than 300 miles. He noted in his diary that it had been a pleasant little journey.

Following his return, Darwin found that the *Beagle* was preparing to sail back to Salvador. There was a significant error in the longitude measurements of both Salvador and Rio, and FitzRoy was determined to put it right once and for all. There was little reason for Darwin to go with the *Beagle*, and he and Augustus Earle made plans to move into temporary quarters ashore until the *Beagle* returned. Two days later the *Beagle* sailed the mile from the city's wharf to a finger of the bay near the village of Botofogo. Darwin spent most of April 25 transferring his belongings and equipment ashore by whaleboat. He nearly lost everything once when the whaleboat was swamped in the surf. "Before my affrighted eyes were floating books, instruments & gun cases & everything which was most useful to me." Everyone jumped to, however, and nothing was lost. But Darwin spent the next day drying out books and clothes and carefully reoiling firearms, microscope, and compass.

At Botofogo he settled down to two months of work. It was an ideal location for studying tropical plants and

Darwin stayed at the village of Botofogo for three months, enjoying a view similar to this sketch by Rugendas. In the background rises pinnacled Corcovado. To Darwin's irritation, Botofogo was one of the favored sites for landing illegal slaves. COURTESY NATIONAL ARCHIVES, RIO DE JANEIRO.

animals and the bold geology near Rio. He could look across a short expanse of water at sentinellike Sugar Loaf Mountain, the glistening rock dome guarding the narrow entrance to the bay. In the opposite direction was pinnacled Corcovado, its peak towering more than 2,000 feet above the city. In his letters home he wrote that he was "red-hot" with spider collecting but that the study of geology "takes the day."

South America's geology was soon to become Darwin's principal concern. By the end of his travels on the continent, he was to confide to a friend that he thought he could write a more thorough geology of South America than had ever been done.

Part of Darwin's enthusiasm can be traced to the influence of Henslow and Sedgwick. But the revolutionary theories of Charles Lyell, a geologist only nine years Darwin's senior, were the strongest influence on an intellect both eager and receptive.

Geological theories were as clouded by the supernatural as those of the origin of species. Much of the inability to explain geological phenomena rationally stemmed from the widespread belief that the earth was much younger than it is. Most scholars, for example, believed that the earth was about 6,000 years old, an age far younger than the estimated 4 billion to 5 billion or more years we know now. James Ussher, the Archbishop of Armagh, precisely placed the creation of the earth at the year 4004 B.C. by counting the generations since Adam as chronicled in the Book of Genesis.

Both Henslow and Sedgwick, like the majority of scientists of their time, believed the earth's surface was a result of a number of divinely sponsored cataclysms, each separated by long periods of calm. During each cataclysm, mammoth floods were supposed to have carved and shaped the earth's surface. The Deluge mentioned in the Bible was thought to be the last of these. To the catastrophists, as adherents to this theory were called, water had done it all.

In a book titled simply *Principles of Geology*, Lyell proposed a daring theory entirely opposed to popular scientific opinion. Developing an idea stated some years earlier by a geologist named James Hutton, Lyell hypothesized that the geological agents observable today— earthquakes, river erosion and deposition, gradual elevation or subsiding of land, lava flows from volcanoes — could explain everything that happened in the history of the earth's surface. According to Lyell, there was no need to resort to divine intervention, if only these agents could be allowed enough time. For Lyell, vast stretches of time were a major part of his theory. Clearly Archbishop Ussher's chronology and Lyell's theory were not compatible. Lyell's work was criticized by the three most prominent geologists in England on the basis that it was inconsistent with the Scriptures.

The first volume of *Principles of Geology*—the work eventually numbered four—was published only a few months before the *Beagle*'s voyage. Oddly enough, it was Henslow who called Darwin's attention to the book and advised him to buy the first volume for the voyage. It would be good reading, said Henslow, but, he added, under no circumstances should Darwin give any account to Lyell's theories.

Darwin finished the book before the *Beagle* had reached St. Jago. The three weeks he spent ashore in St. Jago were with geologist's hammer in hand. Lyell's method seemed to be a superior way to view the landscape. So much could be understood if one admitted the immensity of geological time. When the *Beagle* sailed down the coast of Brazil, his comments reflected his willingness to consider a new idea when it fit the facts, rather than to exclude one because of dogma:

Along the whole coast of Brazil, for a length of at least 2000 miles, and certainly for a considerable space inland, wherever solid rock occurs, it belongs to a granitic formation. . . . Was this effect produced beneath the depths of a profound ocean? . . . Can we believe that any power, acting for a time short of infinity, could have denuded the granite over so many thousand square leagues?

For Darwin, with new ideas but little experience, geology was a gamble, a testing ground for a few cautious speculations. He was more confident in collecting and observing, and while in Brazil, he tried to improve what he already did well. When Darwin received a letter from Henslow mentioning that the museums of England were barren of tropical insect collections, he wrote back for the entomologists to get ready. There would be no better place during the entire voyage for insect collecting. More than any other kind of life, insects are the hallmark of the tropics. On long walks in the forest he caught moths and butterflies. Along beaches and inland marshes he practiced his specialty of collecting beetles.

As he collected, he also sharpened his skill at observation and precise, detailed descriptions of what he caught and what he saw. His most careful observations were of spiders. In proportion to other insects, spiders were more numerous in the tropics than in England. He often sat for hours watching and recording a particular spider's intricate habits. Later he would expand the brief jottings from his pocket notebooks into such meticulous descriptions as this:

I was much interested one day by watching a deadly contest between a Pepsis and a large spider of the genus Lycosa. The wasp made a sudden dash at its prey, and then flew away: the spider was evidently wounded, for, trying to escape, it rolled down a little slope, but had still strength sufficient to crawl into a thick tuft of grass. The wasp soon returned, and seemed surprised at not immediately finding its victim. It then commenced as regular a hunt as ever hound did after fox; making short semicircular casts, and all the time rapidly vibrating its wings and antennae. The spider, although well concealed, was soon discovered; and the wasp, evidently still afraid of its adversary's jaws, after much manoeuvring, inflicted two stings on the under side of its thorax. At last, carefully examining with its antennae the now motionless spider, it proceeded to drag away the body. But I stopped both tyrant and prey.

But the stay in Rio wasn't all work. On May 3 he witnessed the admiral's inspection of the seventy-four-gun battleship H.M.S. *Warspite* and was so excited at the drilled precision of the ship's 400 seamen that he spent the next day dreaming about the "pomp & circumstance of war." He dined with a number of the British merchants who then abounded in Rio and, less to his liking, attended a piano concert with an embassy attaché.

On June 4 the *Beagle* returned from Salvador. Young King ran ahead to Darwin's home in Botofogo to deliver some bad news. Three crewmen who had come down with the "fevers," the nineteenth-century term for malaria, had died. The news struck Darwin hard. He remembered the men well. In his diary he remarked on malaria, which had not yet been diagnosed, nor its connection with the mosquito discovered, referring to the strange and mysterious power of the fevers.

Two days later, Darwin breakfasted aboard the *Beagle* with FitzRoy, catching up on the news. Going on board was a pleasant surprise. It struck him that the *Beagle* had become home and that it was comfortable to be back, although, he noted, "having lived so long on shore, I have almost forgotten how to stow myself in my own corner."

A month later FitzRoy's work in Brazil was finished, and Darwin's collections were bundled for shipment to England. The *Beagle* prepared to sail. On July 5 the rattle of the *Beagle*'s anchor chain echoed across the calm water of Guanabara Bay. With a gentle breeze the *Beagle* slipped beneath Sugar Loaf Mountain into the open sea. The four months in Brazil, wrote Darwin, had passed like as many weeks.

5

A Home for Fuegia Basket
JULY, 1832 —APRIL, 1833

SAILING THE 1,000 miles from Rio de Janeiro south along the coast to the broad estuary of the Río de la Plata, the *Beagle* slowly left the tropics behind. The steep escarpment that had lined the coast of Brazil since Salvador gradually dwindled until half way to the Plata the coast was low, backed by gently rolling hills.

The hills were no longer covered by tropical forests. Cooler temperatures, less rain, and sweeping fires started perhaps by primitive Indians had combined to produce a grassland that spread from southern Brazil across the entire country of Uruguay to the extremities of the Pampas, the flat grassy plain of Argentina which lay west and south of the Plata. Except for the day the *Beagle* passed through a great shoal of porpoises that in places furrowed the whole sea, the passage to the Plata was uneventful.

The Río de la Plata is a gathering of rivers only slightly less gigantic than the Amazon. Rain shed in the Brazilian uplands far to the northeast of the Plata's mouth drains inland, eventually into the Plata's major tributary, the Río Paraná. Another tributary, the Río Paraguay, collects tropical rains from a watershed which, if sloped a few tenths of a degree differently, would pour its waters north to the Amazon. Still another tributary, the Río Pilcomayo, has its beginnings in the streams that flow southeast from the Andes. Together these rivers and a score of lesser ones through countless centuries of geologic time carved a broad lowland between the Brazilian uplands to the east and the Andes to the west. Where the Plata disgorged into the sea, a collection of silt and sediment helped build the Pampas, the broad alluvial plain which sweeps in a wide semicircle from northwest to southwest of the Plata's mouth. In some places the river deposits of the Pampas are 1,000 feet thick.

The Spanish discovered the Río de la Plata in 1512 while looking for a path to the Pacific and eventually explored its tributaries into what is now Bolivia. Twenty-five years later a fort was established at the present site of Buenos Aires, the only place along the mud flats that line the river's edge where a small stream had carved a channel deep enough for the landing of boats. It was an ill-fated attempt. Driven off because of constant harassing by Indians, the Spanish fled the site, leaving behind several dozen head of cattle and a few horses.

The first permanent settlement along the river was 800 miles north at Asunción, established in 1537. Here the Spanish found a warmer, more hospitable climate and friendly Indians. But the mouth of the Plata was strategic. In 1580 settlers descending the river from Asunción succeeded in refounding Buenos Aires. By then wild cattle and horses descending from those left behind by the original settlers roamed the Pampas in large herds.

Compared with the silver pouring from the great Andean mine discovered at Potosí and the rich potential of the highlands, the territory bordering the Plata seemed unimportant. For most of its years under Spanish control, Buenos Aires was but a sentinel guarding the back door to the rich viceroyalty of Peru.

By the time the *Beagle* arrived at the mouth of the Plata, all of the former viceroyalty of the Plata was independent of Spain and had divided itself into separate countries. Argentina's cry for independence had come in 1810, although the Spanish were not finally ousted until six years later. Paraguay had chosen to go its own way in 1811. Uruguay, then called Banda Oriental, which had been attached to Brazil by force when Brazil became independent, fought for freedom with the help of the Argentines in 1825 and was the subject of a war between Argentina and Brazil between 1825 and 1828. Both wanted the strategically placed territory. England finally stepped in to mediate a peace, and in 1828 Banda Oriental became independent.

In place of former colonies there were now countries: in place of the problems brought by the Spanish were those created because the Spanish were gone. Gone was the viceroy, symbol of the Spanish king, and with him the host of ministers and lesser bureaucrats who, for better or worse, had kept the machinery of government running.

Throughout South America, the thinkers and generals who had won independence were unable to guide their countries for long. By 1832 they were all dead or in exile. Simón Bolivar died in 1830, ill and disillusioned, believing that South America was ungovernable. Governing democratically was impractical in the face of illiteracy, economic collapse, and vast Indian populations. Inexperienced in government, the idealists failed. In most countries they were replaced by former military men, who, followed by the troops they had trained and led, were at least organized. Their claim to leadership came from their power.

During the early years following independence, former colonels and powerful regional leaders fought for the dictatorial reins of government, which changed hands often. In 1820 the governorship of Buenos Aires changed twenty times. Argentina, each of its provinces controlled by local strong men, could scarcely be called a country at all. Banda Oriental still feared being gobbled up by the giants on either side, Argentina and Brazil. Bolivia, the most revolutionary of them all, saw its first two presidents murdered in office. By 1832, of the Spanish-speaking countries to be visited by the *Beagle,* only Chile had settled down with a constitution and a peacefully elected president.

As those aboard the *Beagle* were soon to learn, independence had not brought peace to the "horse and cattle countries" near the Plata, as the British called them. On July 26, three weeks after leaving Rio, the *Beagle* sailed into the bay of Montevideo, the tiny capital of Banda Oriental. Just as they were coming to anchor near the

British frigate H.M.S. *Druid,* to everyone's astonishment, the *Druid* signaled the *Beagle* to clear for action and prepare to cover its boats. A few minutes later, six heavily armed boats were preparing to go ashore. The captain of the *Druid* came aboard the *Beagle* and explained that the head of the latest government to take power had confiscated 400 horses belonging to a British subject. His men were going ashore to extract a promise of the horses' return.

He told FitzRoy that things were generally unsettled and that five separate factions were vying for supremacy. The present governor was backed by several hundred cavalry and soldiers, but the strongest of the opposing forces was collecting followers and was soon expected to enter the town. At that point everyone expected the present government to scamper out. "Both parties dislike the sight of blood," wrote Darwin, "& so that the one which appears the strongest gains the day."

FitzRoy's main hope was that the political disturbances wouldn't disrupt his preparations. He hoped in Montevideo to get provisions for one of the most important parts of the voyage, the survey of the coast between the Plata and Tierra del Fuego. Four days after their arrival, however, FitzRoy heard that some old Spanish charts of the Patagonia coast were in Buenos Aires, and he instantly made up his mind to see them. But as Darwin noted in his diary on August 2, peace seemed to fly away from any place the *Beagle* approached.

Nearing Buenos Aires, a guard ship anchored in the channel fired a warning shot. Seeing no reason for a warning, FitzRoy ignored it and sailed on. A moment later the guard ship sent a cannon shot whistling above the *Beagle*'s rigging. Although never having been fired at before, Darwin recalled later that he had no trouble understanding the meaning. Neither did FitzRoy. Before the guard ship could fire again, the *Beagle* was out of range, and FitzRoy was already planning a protest at the least.

At the anchorage they were met by a small boat. The scare of epidemics still made the *Beagle* an unwelcome guest, even though she had been away from England seven months. There was no choice but to return immediately to Montevideo. That was the last slight to FitzRoy's delicate temper. He drafted a note to the captain of the guard ship and to the governor of Buenos Aires to the effect that he had thought he was entering a civilized port. Had he known differently, he would have had a broadside of his own ready as an answer. Then, true to his word, he readied four cannons on one side, and as the *Beagle* sailed out of the harbor, he brought her close by the guard ship. With cannons run out, he hailed that on his return he would be equally prepared, and "if she dared to fire a shot we would send our whole broadside into her rotten hulk." FitzRoy was as angry as only FitzRoy could become, and for once Darwin was in total agreement.

When the *Beagle* returned to Montevideo, FitzRoy managed to have the *Druid* dispatched to Buenos Aires. Orders were to receive a formal apology or to sink the offender. Wrote Darwin in his diary; "Oh I hope the Guard-ship will fire a gun at the Frigate; if she does, it will be her last day above water."

But trouble was not behind them yet. The next day a minister of the present government came aboard the

The main street of Montevideo, the capital of Uruguay, then called Banda Oriental. At the far end of the street is the most important building of any South American seaport, the customs house. At Montevideo, the artist Augustus Earle left the ship because of poor health. This sketch was made by his replacement, Conrad Martens.

Beagle and begged FitzRoy's help to put down an insurrection of some of his own troops. FitzRoy wanted nothing to do with the squabbles between political parties, but he was concerned about protecting private property, especially that belonging to British subjects. He responded by landing thirty sailors and marines ashore. Curious as ever, and by this time sporting a grizzly beard, Darwin went along for a look. They succeeded in taking over the central garrison without firing a shot. Darwin thought the whole enterprise exciting, sharing some of the "reckless gayety," as he termed it, with the sailors.

The following day, however, FitzRoy sensed that a clash would soon take place between the present government and the opposition. Holding the central fort while remaining neutral would be impossible, and he pulled his men back to the ship. A few days later, days so wet and windy that Darwin could do nothing but sit and wait aboard ship, the revolution took place. A few volleys of musketry had done it, and with a magnificent parade, the new governor entered the town. The whole revolution had been rather amusing ("we hear not even one has been wounded") but unsettling ("It makes one ask oneself whether Despotism is not better than such uncontrolled anarchy").

With the change of government and the improving weather, Darwin was able to get ashore. After the glitter and diversity of the tropics Darwin found the country near the Plata uninteresting even at first glance. He characterized the estuary of the river as a wide expanse of muddy water without grandeur or beauty. During the two years the *Beagle* was to spend surveying the coast from the Plata to the tip of land at Tierra del Fuego, Darwin was to return to Buenos Aires and Montevideo a half dozen times. On the rolling hills and plains nearby he would make some of his most complete collections and important discoveries. But these he would have to wait. The *Beagle* was heading for the coast of Patagonia. Darwin would not have an opportunity to study in detail the land near the Plata for nine months, much of it, to his pain, spent at sea.

During these months the *Beagle* retraced the same path as the expedition of 1826. By mid-September the *Beagle* had arrived at Bahía Blanca, a small military post on the coast 300 miles south of the Plata. To help speed the survey of the coast, FitzRoy chartered two small schooners, the *La Paz* and the *Libre.* Then while he supervised modifications of the two boats, Darwin roamed the countryside, trading briskly with the soldiers of a small fort for ostriches and their eggs, deer, and armadillos. But the stay was short. FitzRoy put Darwin's chart room mate Stokes in charge of the *La Paz* and Wickham, with whom he often hunted, in command of the *Libre.*

On Wednesday, October 17, the small fleet sailed. The smaller ships turned south to survey the coast between Bahía Blanca and the Río Negro. Darwin was sorry for the separation, commenting, "Our society on board can ill afford to lose such very essential members." The *Beagle* turned north for the Plata once again. The ships would meet the end of the following month at the mouth of the Río Negro before voyaging to Tierra del Fuego to carry out a special part of FitzRoy's mission.

The weeks before their rendezvous were busy ones.

First, the *Beagle* returned to Buenos Aires, this time to be received more civilly. FitzRoy still wanted to have a look at the Spanish charts of the coast, which, as inaccurate as they were, would be something of a guide. Buenos Aires, too, would have to provide the last joys of civilization they would have in quite a while.

It was Darwin's first visit to the city. The growth of the cattle industry and the increase of trade during the last years of the Spanish Empire had raised the city's population to 60,000. The days of fastest growth, however, were still to come, for all of the Plata was just beginning to discover itself, or rather to allow itself to be discovered by the great trading nations of Europe, mainly England. Darwin described the city thus:

> The city of Buenos Ayres is large; and I should think one of the most regular in the world. Every street is at right angles to the one it crosses . . . the houses are collected into solid squares of equal dimensions, which are called quadras. On the other hand, the houses themselves are hollow squares; all the rooms opening into a neat little courtyard. They are generally only one story high, with flat roofs, which are fitted with seats, and are much frequented by the inhabitants in summer. In the centre of the town is the Plaza, where the public offices, fortress, cathedral, &c., stand. Here also, the old viceroys, before the revolution, had their palaces. The general assemblage of buildings possesses considerable architectural beauty, although none individually can boast of any.

The British influence was more apparent in Buenos Aires than in Rio. There were shops owned by Englishmen filled with English goods, and Darwin enjoyed some shopping there, as well as his more official tasks of finding what information he could on the geology of the country. As Darwin had already noted, many of the English in South America were not always of the highest caliber, and there was more than the usual number of adventurers, conniving merchants, and a rogue or two. On November 9 he and FitzRoy called on one such character, the Englishwoman Mrs. Clarke:

The history of this woman is most strange. She was originally a handsome young woman, transported for some atrocious crime. On board the convict ship on its passage outwards, . . . sometime before coming to the Latitude of Buenos Ayres she planned with the rest of the convict women to murder all on board excepting a few sailors. She with her own hands killed the Captain, & by the help of a few sailors brought the ship into Buenos Ayres. After this she married a man of considerable property & now inherits it. Everybody seems to have forgotten her crimes . . . Mrs. Clarke is now an old decrepid woman: with a masculine face, & evidently even yet a most ferocious mind. Her commonest expressions are "I would hang them all, Sir." "I would kill him, Sir." For smaller offenses, "I would cut their fingers off." The worthy old lady looks as if she would rather do it, than say so.

The following day the *Beagle* left for Montevideo, and after five miserable days beating "as foul a wind as ever blew" the anchor was dropped with relief. Mail from home scarcely four months old was waiting for Darwin. While the *Beagle* crowded provisions aboard, he took a day to go galloping over the grassy plains before settling down to pack more collections for shipment to Henslow.

He also received the second volume of Lyell's *Principles of Geology*. It didn't appear as useful to him as the first volume had been. Most of it was concerned not with the practical aspects of geology but rather with some of the theoretical problems of species and evolution. In any case, he would have plenty of time to read it, probably more than once, on the long voyage south. By late November the *Beagle* was ready for the sail to Tierra del Fuego. Wrote Darwin: "I am glad of it, for I am impatient to be again at sea."

The several large mountainous islands which make up Tierra del Fuego are geologically part of the South American continent. They are separated from the mainland, however, by the Strait of Magellan. In the days before the Panama Canal, the southernmost point of Tierra del Fuego, named Cape Horn, was the corner on the path from Europe to the entire west coast of the Americas as well as the whaling grounds of the Pacific. The weather of the Horn was notoriously foul. Icy gales almost continuously whip the seas into mountainous waves that lash the open ocean south of the Horn. As an alternative, ships could wend their way in the lee of Tierra del Fuego's islands through narrow rockbound channels to escape the fierce storms. The French had mapped the Strait of Magellan in the 1790's. Still, the accurate charting of the coast and jagged channels had been left undone until King and FitzRoy started the task during the first expedition.

Despite the fierce climate and inhospitable landscape, Tierra del Fuego was inhabited by Indians, four separate tribes that totaled no more than 8,000 people. Darwin later described them as being "in a lower state of improvement than in any other part of the world." During the first expedition in 1828, the Indians had given FitzRoy a problem. At one point during that survey, a whaleboat had been stolen, endangering the lives of some of FitzRoy's men. Both in retaliation and to retrieve the boat, FitzRoy sent armed men ashore, eventually taking two men and a young girl hostage. Unable to find the boat, he finally ended up taking the hostages and a young boy a crewman had purchased for a pearl button back with him to England. Though one man died of smallpox, FitzRoy had the others educated at his own expense.

They now sported the names York Minster, Jemmy Button, and Fuegia Basket. It was FitzRoy's intention to return them to their homes, bringing to the primitive Indians of Tierra del Fuego these seeds of civilization. A missionary named Matthews was to be landed with them. On December 17, 1832, the *Beagle* anchored at Good Success Bay, at the easternmost tip of Tierra del Fuego. Wrote Darwin:

While entering we were saluted in a manner becoming the inhabitants of this savage land. A group of Fuegians partly concealed by the entangled forest, were perched on a wild point overhanging the sea; and as we passed by, they sprang up and waving their tattered cloaks sent forth a loud and sonorous shout. The savages followed the ship, and just before dark we saw their fire, and again heard their wild cry. . . .

The next day FitzRoy sent a party ashore, Darwin among them, to communicate with the Fuegians. Face to face with Indians covered only by guanaco skin capes, alternately babbling and mimicking the gestures of the crew, was without doubt, wrote Darwin, the most curious and interesting spectacle he had ever seen. "I could not have believed how wide was the difference between savage and civilized man."

These Indians were not the tribe of any of FitzRoy's Indians; hence the *Beagle* remained in Good Success Bay only four days. With his interest in the Indians and the careful descriptions he recorded in his journal of their habits and manners, Darwin had time only for a brief study of the country, noting:

There was a degree of mysterious grandeur in mountain behind mountain, with the deep intervening valleys, all covered by one thick, dusky mass of forest. The atmosphere, likewise, in this climate, where gale succeeds gale, with rain, hail, and sleet, seems blacker than anywhere else.

FitzRoy planned to land York Minster and his future wife, Fuegia Basket, with York's own people near Waterman Island, in the western part of Tierra del Fuego, then on his return eastward to put Jemmy Button ashore on the western end of Navarin Island. On December 21 FitzRoy navigated the *Beagle* out of Good Success Bay. Two days of clear weather and strong easterly winds enabled the *Beagle* to round Cape Horn without problems. Then the weather changed, and the storms for which the region was famous returned.

Under leaden skies the *Beagle* fought westward against winds reaching near gale force. Rain squall fol-

The *Beagle* in the Strait of Magellan.

lowed rain squall. After two days of such weather, FitzRoy maneuvered the *Beagle* into a small cove not far from the Horn. There they spent Christmas Day 1832, remaining an additional four days while storms raged in the open sea.

The last day of the year FitzRoy decided to venture west once again. For the next thirteen days the *Beagle* beat against strong easterly winds, making little progress. On January 12 the sky was so overcast that FitzRoy was unable to take a reading on the sun, leaving him to doubt their position. Lookouts were posted on the leeward deck to keep a sharp eye for white water, lest they be blown aground.

On the thirteenth the storm worsened, the horizon hidden by sheets of icy rain. It was the worst gale FitzRoy had ever experienced. Darwin, in misery, lay in his hammock "scarcely for an hour free from seasickness." In his diary he added: "Spirit, temper and stomach will not hold out much longer." In the late morning FitzRoy turned the *Beagle* into the wind, hoping to ride out the storm. It was then the *Beagle* had its worst moment. As Darwin wrote later:

At noon a great sea broke over us, and filled one of the whale-boats, which was obliged to be instantly cut away. The poor *Beagle* trembled at the shock, and for a few minutes would not obey her helm; but soon, like a good ship that she was, she righted and came up to the wind again. Had another sea followed the first, our fate would have been decided soon, and forever. . . .

A Fuegian Indian. Darwin thought the Indians of Tierra del Fuego were the most primitive creatures he had ever seen.

With everyone fatigued and many of Darwin's collections soaked, FitzRoy finally gave up trying to reach western Tierra del Fuego. With York Minster's agreement, FitzRoy decided to put all the Fuegians ashore with the tribe of Jemmy Button. He immediately set a new course for the mouth of the Beagle Channel, a narrow strait of water discovered on the first expedition. By January 19 they were close to their destination. For the final leg of the journey the *Beagle* was anchored, and an expedition of twenty-eight men —Darwin, FitzRoy, the Fuegians, crew, and the Reverend Matthews —set out in the yawl and two whaleboats.

A few days later they made contact with Jemmy Button's tribe and at his suggestion set up a camp at Woolya, on the east side of Navarin Island. To the consternation of both FitzRoy and Darwin, Jemmy's welcome by family and tribe was indifferent. Jemmy himself had completely forgotten the language. Still the party spent several days ashore, constructing houses for the Fuegians and Matthews and transferring the trade goods he had brought as an added lure for the Indians. As Darwin noted, it was perhaps a foolish collection of articles —wineglasses, tea trays, soup bowls, white linen, beaver hats, and the like —inappropriate for that country, but tempting nevertheless. Then the small expedition left, FitzRoy sending the yawl and one whaleboat back to the *Beagle*. He and Darwin took the other off for a week of exploring.

Everywhere they went, they saw scattered groups of Indians or found the deserted wigwams made of sticks and mud, and Darwin was visibly reminded of their primitive, precariously balanced way of life. One crewman said, not entirely in jest, that they simply had to be a different species of life from Englishmen. Darwin's diary was filled with notes on "the most abject and miserable creatures I anywhere beheld." On coming across a group more pitiable than most, he wrote:

These poor wretches were stunted in their growth, their hideous faces bedaubed with white paint, their skins filthy and greasy, their hair entangled, their voices discordant, and their gestures violent. Viewing such men, one can hardly make oneself believe that they are fellow-creatures, and inhabitants of the same world. . . . Whenever it is low water, winter or summer, night or day, they must rise to pick shellfish from the rocks; and the women either dive to collect sea-eggs, or sit patiently in their canoes, and with a baited hairline without any hook, jerk out little fish. If a seal is killed, or the floating carcass of a putrid whale discovered, it is a feast; and such miserable food is assisted by a few tasteless berries and fungi.

They returned to the settlement February 6. They found chaos and the Reverend Matthews in fear for his life, with good reason. From the day Darwin and FitzRoy had left, new groups of Indians had begun to arrive. York and Jemmy, proud of the articles and gadgets brought from England were eager to show every newcomer the objects of their wealth. The step from envy to plunder was a short one, quickly taken. Darwin describes the scene thusly:

York and Jemmy lost many things, and Matthews almost everything which had not been concealed underground. Every article seemed to have been torn up and divided by the natives. Matthews described the watch he was obliged always to keep as most harassing; night and day he was surrounded by the natives, who tried to tire him out by making an incessant noise close to his head. One day an old man, whom Matthews asked to leave his wigwam, immediately returned with a large stone in his hand: another day a whole party came armed with stones and stakes, and some of the younger men and Jemmy's brother were crying: Matthews met them with presents. Another party showed by signs that they wished to strip him naked and pluck out all the hairs of his face and body. I think we arrived just in time to save his life. Jemmy's relatives had been so vain and foolish, that they had showed to strangers their plunder, and their manner of obtaining it. It was quite melancholy leaving the three Fuegians with their savage countrymen; but it was a great comfort that they had no personal fears. York, being a powerful resolute man, was pretty sure to get on well, together with his wife Fuegia. Poor Jemmy looked rather disconsolate, and would then, I have little doubt, have been glad to have returned with us. . . . Our three Fuegians, though they have been only three years with civilized men, would, I am sure, have been glad to have retained their new habits; but this was obviously impossible. I fear it is more than doubtful, whether their visit will have been of any use to them.

Taking Matthews with them, they returned in the whaleboat to the *Beagle.* Covering more than 300 miles, they had been gone for twenty days. FitzRoy planned to return briefly the following year to put the finishing touches on the survey of Tierra del Fuego as well as to look in on the three Fuegians. For better or worse, his obligation was fulfilled, though he was far from satisfied with the outcome. The *Beagle* set a course north, leaving

Another view of the Indians of Tierra del Fuego. From a drawing by Captain P. P. King, commander of the first expedition.

the icy waters of Tierra del Fuego behind them, at least temporarily.

Five hundred miles northeast of Cape Horn lie the Falkland Islands. Discovered by the English, later colonized briefly by the French, the islands had been claimed in 1820 by the Argentines, who called them the Malvinas. But by March 1, 1833, when the *Beagle* dropped anchor in Berkeley Harbor, all hands were surprised to see the Union Jack flying. In the brief time since the *Beagle* had left Plymouth, England had reasserted her claim to the islands, and a British officer was in charge of the population, which numbered about twenty-five men, "of which more than half," reported Darwin, "were rebels and murderers."

To replace the *La Paz* and the *Libre*, which were too small for work away from the shore, FitzRoy here bought a 170-ton schooner, which he named the *Adventure* after the *Beagle*'s sailing mate on the first expedition. Waiting for neither Admiralty approval nor money, FitzRoy paid for the *Adventure* from his own pocket, expecting reimbursement later. It was an act that would later cause FitzRoy more than a share of anguish. At the time, however, the *Adventure* was a welcome remedy for the *Beagle*'s lack of space. The *Adventure* needed refitting, and with winter coming, FitzRoy headed his convoy back to Banda Oriental. In the meantime, the *Beagle* set off in search of the two schooners still surveying the coast of Patagonia. Unable to find them but hearing that all was well, the *Beagle*, too, took the northward course.

Darwin decided to spend the next months at Maldonado, the small village east of Montevideo near the site

FitzRoy had chosen for the *Adventure*'s modifications. It would give him a chance to catch up on the entries in his diary and to study the plants and animals of the grasslands.

From Maldonado on June 2, 1833, Darwin wrote to his friend John Herbert. "Tierra del Fuego," he said, "is indeed a miserable place. . . . Heaven knows everyone in the *Beagle* has seen enough in this one summer to last them their natural lives."

6

A Lions' Provider

APRIL, 1833–JULY, 1833

THE SAIL from the Falkland Islands was long and hard. By April the *Beagle* had made its way back to Montevideo, then on to Maldonado. Darwin noted, "During our absence things have been going on pretty quietly with the exception of a few revolutions."

Darwin characterized Maldonado as dull, quiet and forlorn: "It possesses scarcely any trade; the exports being confined to a few hides and living cattle. The inhabitants are chiefly land owners, together with a few shopkeepers and the necessary tradesmen, such as blacksmiths and carpenters. . . . "

Like all small villages throughout Argentina and Banda Oriental, Maldonado was a servant to the cattle *estancias* that spread over the nearby countryside. In Banda Oriental, as in the other South American countries, the only basis for wealth and prestige was land.

The value of cattle dated to about fifty years before Darwin's arrival. Since the first cattle and horses had been left behind by the Spanish, they had multiplied into millions, wandering over massive unfenced tracts of land,

A gaucho intends to bring down a rhea with the bola.
COURTESY AMERICAN MUSEUM OF NATURAL HISTORY.

the common property of anyone who wanted them. One estimate places the number of cattle then on the Pampas at 80,000,000. In the villages, wild horses were such a menace that slaves were often assigned the task of killing them by knife. As time went on, the wild cattle became the sustenance of life to the seminomadic cowboy called the gaucho. Where cattle and horses roamed, from the grasslands of southern Brazil to the southernmost limits of the Pampas, there could be found the gaucho, living almost on horseback. The gauchos slaughtered cattle where they found them, stripped off the hides, and, after taking a portion of the best meat to satisfy their seemingly endless hunger for fresh beef, left the carcasses to the wolves and carrion hawks.

By the time of Darwin's visit, although the salting of beef had given rise to a cattle industry, an estimated 1,000,000 head of cattle a year were still slaughtered in Banda Oriental for their hides only, the meat literally going to rot. As for horses, Darwin wrote: "Animals are so abundant in these countries, that humanity and self-interest are not closely united." The general disregard for horses was illustrated to Darwin one day as he was riding with a wealthy landowner:

. . . my horse, being tired, lagged behind. The man often shouted to me to spur him. When I remonstrated that it was a pity, for the horse was quite exhausted, he cried out, "Why not?—never mind—spur him—it is *my* horse. *I* had then some difficulty in making him comprehend that it was for the horse's sake, and not on his account, that I did not choose to use my spurs. He exclaimed, with a look of great surprise, "Ah, Don

Carlos, que cosa!" It was clear that such an idea had never before entered his head.

The process of salting beef brought a change to the Pampas and Banda Oriental and the beginnings of prosperity. Central places with slaughterhouses and salting stations quickly gave rise to the idea of definite land holdings and permanent herds. Large cattle *estancias* became a more permanent part of the landscape outside the cities, and by 1833 nearly all of Banda Oriental was divided into *estancias*, although many *estancieros* barely knew the boundaries of their own land. Like the sugar or coffee *fazendeiro* of Brazil, the cattle *estanciero* was the aristocrat of his time.

The gauchos sometimes worked for the *estanciero*, herding and counting his cattle or breaking his horses, but the routine life and the pattern of *estancia* living never entirely suited the gauchos' temperament. Sometimes they chose to work, sometimes not. Wherever the *estancias* dwindled off near the frontier, gauchos could be found living their old way of life, feeding on the wild cattle which still roamed in abundance.

Darwin spent about ten weeks near Maldonado, nearly the same length of time as he had spent in Rio. But instead of insects and geology, this time he concentrated on animals, birds, and reptiles, making a "nearly perfect collection." At Maldonado he was able to make better use of his time, thanks to the generosity of FitzRoy.

At Banda Oriental, FitzRoy assigned a young cabin boy named Sims Covington as Darwin's assistant. Darwin taught Covington how to shoot and stuff birds, and he became in time "a very accurate person." This freed Darwin from some of the more mechanical aspects of collecting and allowed him to spend more time on his diary.

While the *Adventure* was being refitted, Darwin set out on one of his excursions, taking along young Covington. The trip gave Darwin a good chance to see life on the *estancias* and a look at the manners of the gaucho:

. . . I will give an account of a little excursion I made as far as the river Polanco, which is about seventy miles distant, in a northerly direction. I may mention, as a proof how cheap everything is in this country, that I paid only two dollars a day, or eight shillings, for two men, together with a troop of about a dozen riding-horses. My companions were well armed with pistols and sabres; a precaution which I thought rather unnecessary; but the first piece of news we heard was, that, the day before, a traveller from Monte Video had been found dead on the road, with his throat cut. This happened close to a cross, the record of a former murder.

On the first night we slept at a retired little country-house; and there I soon found out that I possessed two or three articles, especially a pocket compass, which created unbounded astonishment. In every house I was asked to show the compass, and by its aid, together with a map, to point out the direction of various places. It excited the liveliest admiration that I, a perfect stranger, should know the road (for direction and road are are synonymous in this open country) to places where I had never been. At one house a young woman, who was ill in bed, sent to entreat me to come and show her the compass. If their surprise was great, mine was greater, to find such ignorance among people who possessed their thousands of cattle and "estancias" of great extent. It can only be accounted for by the circumstances that this retired part of the country is seldom visited by foreigners. I was asked whether the earth or sun moved; whether it was hotter or colder to the north; where Spain was, and many other such questions. The greater number of the inhabitants had an indistinct idea that England, London, and North America, were different names for the same place; but the better informed well knew that London and North America were separate countries close together, and that England was a large town in London! . . . The astonishment at the compass, and my other feats in jugglery, was to a certain degree advantageous, as with that, and the long stories my guides told of my breaking stones, knowing venomous from harmless snakes, collecting insects, etc., I repaid them for their hospitality. I am writing as if I had been among the inhabitants of central Africa: Banda Oriental would not be flattered by the comparison; but such were my feelings at the time.

The next day the party rode to the tiny village of Las Minas through country so thinly inhabited they encountered scarcely a soul. Both Banda Oriental and Argentina were underpopulated in the sense that the rich lands could support far more people. Their combined population totaled slightly more than 1,000,000, one fourth of Brazil's.

Despite the apparent dangers of traveling in these countries, Darwin everywhere found extraordinary courtesy toward him, even if it was mixed with curiosity. To find a place to stay for the night was as easy as stopping at the nearest *estancia*. A certain form of politeness was necessary in the request, but the result could usually be predicted:

On approaching the house of a stranger, it is usual to follow several little points of etiquette: riding up slowly to the door, the salutation of Ave Maria is given, and until somebody comes out and asks you to alight, it is not customary even to get off your horse. . . . Having entered the house, some general conversation is kept up for a few minutes, till permission is asked to pass the night there. This is granted as a matter of course. The stranger then takes his meals with the family, and a room is assigned him, where with the horsecloths belonging to his recado (or saddle of the Pampas) he makes his bed. . . .

Beyond the courtesy found everywhere during this expedition, he was surprised how little the crude wealth of the *estanciero* was reflected in anything but land and cattle. One *estanciero* with thousands of head of cattle tended by a large crew of men had a crudely constructed house with a mud floor and windows without glass. The furniture, had the man been a Brazilian coffee baron, would have been French; here it was a few chairs and stools with a couple of tables. The food was often the most simple imaginable, beef with pumpkin or corn, served without bread or wine.

One delightful exception was the arrival of the party at the *estancia* of Sebastián de Pimiento, "a fine old Cavallero."

His house was better furnished than any I had seen; this probably was owing to the presence of some pretty Signoritas, his daughters. These same young ladies are universally quite out of character with the rest of the house. They are dressed exceedingly well: and their whole appearance & manner is very lady-like. Yet with all this, as in Pimiento's house, they superintend all the cooking & perform some of the lowest menial offices. One of the greatest inconveniences in the manners of these people, is the quantity you are obliged to eat: time after time they pile heaps of meat on your plate; after having [eaten] a great deal too much & having skilfully arranged what is left so as to make as little show as possible, a charming Signorita will perhaps present you with a choice piece from her own plate with her own fork; this you must eat, let the consequences be what it may, for it is a high compliment. Oh the difficulty of smiling sweet thanks. . . .

Of the people of Argentina and Banda Oriental the gaucho took Darwin's fancy the most. Wherever cattle and horses were found, there were the gauchos. During his land travels the following two years, Darwin frequently used them as guides, recording much in his pocket notebooks and journal about their skills and habits. One of his earliest encounters with the gaucho was at a small *pulpería* —a gaucho's place to learn news, tell stories, drink and while away the time —near the village of Las Minas, the second day of the excursion up the Río Polanco. Darwin describes it thusly:

During the evening a great number of Gauchos came in to drink spirits and smoke cigars: their appearance is very striking; they are generally tall and handsome; but with a proud and dissolute expression of countenance. They frequently wear their moustaches, and long black hair curling down their backs. With their brightly-coloured garments, great spurs clanking about their heels, and knives stuck as daggers (and often so used) at their waists, they look a very different race of men from what might be expected from their name of

Gauchos, or simple countrymen. Their politeness is excessive; they never drink their spirits without expecting you to taste it; but whilst making their exceedingly graceful bow, they seem quite as ready, if occasion offered, to cut your throat.

In nothing was the pride of the gaucho more apparent than in his handling of horses. In the rough life on flat plains a horse was life, enabling the gaucho to find his food, earn his living, and on frequent occasions escape the ever-present Indians. Yet the gaucho's handling of horses, like his manners and dress, involved apparent disdain and practiced effortlessness. Observed Darwin:

The Gauchos are well known to be perfect riders. The idea of being thrown, let the horse do what it likes, never enters their head. Their criterion of a good rider is, a man who can manage an untamed colt, or who, if his horse falls, alights on his own feet, or can perform other such exploits. I have heard of a man betting that he would throw his horse down twenty times, and that nineteen times he would not fall himself. I recollect seeing a Gaucho riding a very stubborn horse, which three times successively reared so high as to fall backwards with great violence. The man judged with uncommon coolness the proper moment for slipping off, not an instant before or after the right time. . . . The Gaucho never appears to exert any muscular force. . . .

No one was more at home in his environment than the gaucho, and Darwin gave great value to their observations of nature. He learned from them the habits of Indians and animals of the plains and hill country and such assorted facts as that the common deer of the Pampas loses its taint when buried in fresh soil. On the long cross-country rides he learned to enjoy smoking the Gaucho's strong cigars and sipping a cup of *maté* tea.

A gaucho campsite on the Pampas. The men at the right are preparing the meat, often the only item in the gaucho's diet for days on end. Their dress is typical of what Darwin encountered. COURTESY NATIONAL ARCHIVES, RIO DE JANEIRO.

Some of the things that Darwin learned from the gaucho, outside of the nature of science, brought him almost more pain than pleasure. Such was his learning to throw the bolas. The bolas were used by the gaucho, along with the lasso, for catching all kinds of animals from the ostrich to wild cattle. Depending on the animals sought, the bolas were either two or three balls of iron or stone, covered with leather and tied together by a braided leather thong about eight feet long.

The Gaucho holds the smallest of the three in his hand, and whirls the other two round and round his head; then, taking aim, sends them like chain shot revolving through the air. The balls no sooner strike any object, than, winding round it, they cross each other, and become firmly hitched. . . . The main difficulty . . . is to ride so well as to be able at full speed, and while suddenly turning about, to whirl them so steadily round the head, as to take aim: on foot any person would soon learn the art. One day, as I was amusing myself by galloping and whirling the balls round my head, by accident the free one struck a bush; and its revolving motion being thus destroyed, it immediately fell to the ground, and like magic caught one hind leg of my horse; the other ball was then jerked out of my hand, and the horse fairly secured. . . . The Gauchos roared with laughter; they cried out that they had seen every sort of animal caught, but had never before seen a man caught by himself.

Near Maldonado, Darwin was quick to notice the changes in the natural habitat brought about by man. Although he failed to realize it at the time, the almost complete absence of trees may have been man's doing. Darwin noticed that the rainfall of Banda Oriental seemed adequate for trees and that the peach and olive trees introduced by the Spanish grew easily. From this he speculated that one might have to look for some unknown cause to explain the presence of the grasslands. Perhaps because he had observed there were no longer Indians — wild or otherwise —in Banda Oriental, he overlooked them as a possible cause. In all probability much of the grassland of the Pampas and Banda Oriental resulted as a second growth after the burning off of the scrub forest by the primitive Indians, either on purpose or accidentally. The native mammals of Banda Oriental also reflected the presence of man. Wrote Darwin:

. . . the only one now left of any size . . . is the Cervus campestris. This deer is exceedingly abundant, often in small herds, throughout the countries bordering the Plata and in Northern Patagonia. If a person crawling close along the ground, slowly advances towards a herd, the deer frequently, out of curiosity, approach to reconnoitre him. I have by this means killed, from one spot, three out of the same herd. Although so tame and inquisitive, yet when approached on horseback, they are exceedingly wary. In this country nobody goes on foot, and the deer knows man as its enemy only when he is mounted and armed with the bolas. . . .

In addition to mammals, Darwin also collected nine species of snakes, more common in the grasslands than the tropical forests of Brazil, and with the help of Sims Covington, eighty kinds of birds and a number of rodents. One of these, the capybara, is the world's largest gnawing animal; Darwin shot one in Montevideo weighing ninety-eight pounds. Of the birds, wrote Darwin:

The number, tameness, and disgusting habits of the carrion-feeding hawks of South America make them pre-eminently striking to any one accustomed only to the birds of Northern Europe. . . . In their habits they well supply the place of our carrion-crows, magpies, and ravens; a tribe of birds widely distributed over the rest of the world, but entirely absent in South America.

Darwin's stay at Maldonado marked a year and a half that the *Beagle* had been away from England, and the experience had so far seemed to make him more and more curious. His notations increasingly compared the species of one region with another, and he was mystified by how alike different species in adjacent regions could be, yet so different from the ones he knew from Europe. Why were the capybaras similar to other South American rodents but so different from the muskrat of Europe? Why was there a particular species of carrion-feeding birds, built on some apparently South American design, but no magpies or crows? The then popular theory of species did little to explain what he saw. As he had learned from Sedgwick, wasn't the test of a good theory that it explained observable facts? At Maldonado, Darwin had begun to ask questions, at least to himself, but still without an inkling of where the answers would lead him.

But a year and a half away from home had also taken its toll. His letters reflected that he missed his family and friends, and his spirits occasionally flagged. The prospect of what he was still to see kept him going at those moments. "If I was to throw it away," he wrote Catherine from Maldonado, "I don't think I should ever rest quiet in my grave. I certainly should be a ghost and haunt the

British Museum." By then, too, his careful collections and parts of his journal had begun to arouse interest among scientists in England. If he himself was aware of this, he failed to show it in his letters. To Herbert he wrote from Maldonado on June 2, 1833, "You rank my Natural History labours far too high. I am nothing more than a lions' provider: I do not feel it all sure that they will not growl and finally destroy me."

In a letter to Catherine, however, he did drop a hint about what might be a nice future life when he wrote, ". . . it appears to me the doing what *little* we can to increase the general stock of knowledge is as respectable an object of life as one can in any likelihood pursue." But even these thoughts about the work and excitement of the voyage were few. In any case, his choices for a career, if he had them, would have to wait until the end of the voyage. They had not yet finished the survey of the coast of Patagonia.

FitzRoy was as restless as Darwin to be around the Horn once and for all. He told Darwin at Maldonado that he hoped to make it by the end of the year. Part of his reason for buying the *Adventure* had been to shorten the time-consuming job of surveying. With the *Adventure* still not ready, FitzRoy's anxiety got the best of him, and in mid-July he took the *Beagle* once more south along the coast toward the Río Negro, Darwin aboard, anxious to see new country. He would return only once more to Banda Oriental, five months later, but then only after riding through dangerous Indian country and getting caught by a revolution in Buenos Aires.

7

Indians and Rosas
AUGUST, 1833

ON AUGUST 3, 1833, the *Beagle* arrived at the mouth of the Río Negro, the principal river on the east coast between the Plata and the Strait of Magellan. Fifty years before, the Spanish had founded a small village 18 miles inland to mine salt from nearby flats for export to the slaughterhouses and salting sheds of Buenos Aires. The village, called indifferently by its inhabitants either El Carmen or Patagones, was still the most southerly civilized settlement on the entire coast. Situated at the northern edge of the bleak and gravelly Patagonian plateau, salt remained El Carmen's only reason for being.

It was Darwin's plan to travel from the mouth of the Río Negro inland to El Carmen, then journey by horseback 80 miles north to Bahía Blanca, the small army post the *Beagle* had visited the previous September. There he would rendezvous with the *Beagle,* which meanwhile would survey its way along the coast. Not realizing it then, Darwin was to see the beginnings of the bloody campaigns against the Indians that were to plague Argentina for fifty years. The Indians that roamed Argentina's plains —the Abipone and the Puelche —were more war-like than either the highlands Indians of the Altiplano or the more primitive forest tribes of Brazil. With the Arau-canians of Chile, the Indians of Argentina were more like those of the Great Plains and prairies of the United States. They had learned quickly to ride the wild horses aban-doned by the Spanish, and in a generation or two it had changed their pattern of life. Ranging far wider on their hunting grounds than before, they depleted the guanaco and the ostrich, then readily took to hunting the wild cattle that had also been generously provided by the Spanish.

Like the Plains Indians of the United States, they fought invaders of their land. The Indians of Argentina stopped the southerly advance of the Incas. When the Spanish arrived, they thwarted the first attempts of the Spanish to settle near the Plata. Even when Buenos Aires had become a city of 30,000 people, late in the years of the Spanish Empire, the Indians raided its outskirts, stealing thousands of head of cattle each year. During Argentina's war for independence they further took ad-vantage of the disorganization to attack the *estancias* that had begun to move south of Buenos Aires into the Pampas. Like the sentiment in the United States during the 1870's, the Argentines believed that settlement would never come to the fertile grasslands until the Indians were exterminated.

The wars of extermination had scarcely begun when Darwin arrived. But the scars of many a former skirmish were apparent as he set off from the *Beagle* toward the village of El Carmen:

On the way we passed the ruins of some fine "estancias," which a few years since had been destroyed by the Indians. They withstood several attacks. A man present at one gave me a very lively description of what took place. The inhabitants had sufficient notice to drive all the cattle and horses into the "corral" which surrounded the house, and likewise to mount some small cannon. The Indians were Araucanians from the south of Chile; several hundreds in number, and highly disciplined. They first appeared in two bodies on a neighbouring hill; having there dismounted, and taken off their fur mantles, they advanced naked to the charge. The only weapon of an Indian is a very long bamboo or chuzo, ornamented with ostrich feathers, and pointed by a sharp spear-head. My informer seemed to remember with the greatest horror the quivering of these chuzos as they approached near. When close, the cacique Pincheira hailed the besieged to give up their arms, or he would cut all their throats. As this would probably have been the result of their entrance under any circumstances, the answer was given by a volley of musketry. The Indians, with great steadiness, came to the very fence of the corral: but to their surprise they found the posts fastened together by iron nails instead of leather thongs, and, of course, in vain attempted to cut them with their knives. This saved the lives of the Christians: many of the wounded Indians were carried away by their companions. . . . They retired to their horses, and seemed to hold a council of war. This was an awful pause for the Spaniards, as all their ammunition, with the exception of a few cartridges, was expended. In an instant the Indians mounted their horses, and galloped out of sight. Another attack was still more quickly repulsed. A cool Frenchman managed the gun; he stopped till the Indians approached close, and then raked their line with grapeshot: he thus laid thirty-nine of them on the ground; and, of course, such a blow immediately routed the whole party.

Arriving at El Carmen, Darwin found it a small village of a few hundred people, a large number of them partially civilized Indians. He stayed long enough to view the salina where salt was collected, then pressed northward to the Río Colorado, the southern boundary of the Pampas. He left August 11, 1833, with an Englishman named Harris as guide, and five gauchos.

The first day, still on the northern fringe of Patagonia, they rode across gravelly soils tufted with brown desert grasses. Here and there low, thorny bushes dotted the landscape. Occasionally the trail led past muddy, shallow wells, their brackish water the key to life on the plains. The first night they made camp near a strange tree. Darwin was told by one of the gauchos that the Indians revered the tree as an alter to their gods, leaving offerings tied to its branches as they passed it. Here, as they were making camp, one of the gauchos spied a single cow, chased down the unfortunate wanderer, and slaughtered it.

We here had the four necessaries of life "en el campo,"— pasture for the horses, water (only a muddy puddle), meat and fire-wood. The Gauchos were in high spirits at finding all these luxuries; and we soon set to work at the poor cow. This was the first night which I passed under the open sky. . . . There is high enjoyment in the independence of the Gaucho life—to be able at any moment to pull up your horse, and say, "Here we will pass the night." The death-like stillness of the plain, the dogs keeping watch, the gipsy-group of Gauchos making their beds round the fire, have left in my mind a strongly-marked picture of this night, which will never be forgotten.

The next day they continued across similar country. For Darwin the land was a disappointment, nearly devoid of birds or animals. Occasionally they saw deer or guanaco, but Darwin noted the agouti, a coyotelike animal, was the commonest animal of the entire region, "a true friend of the desert." The following day they approached the Río Colorado. Here the landscape began to change, and some miles north of the Río Colorado it was once again that of the Pampas. The plains here had grass and long clover, the winter rains sprinkling the turf with flowers. Here also, encamped close to the banks of the river, was the army of General Rosas.

General Juan Emmanuel Rosas was forty when Darwin met him near the Río Colorado. By then he was already a powerful *caudillo* —a regional leader with a large personal following. Three years later he would become governor of Buenos Aires for the second time and unite Argentina under a powerful, cruel dictatorship.

The Argentine Confederation in 1833 was far from being as united as the name would suggest. Though geographically similar to the Argentina of today, the confederation was really four separate regions, each with its own interests to protect and its own *caudillos* jealous of power. First and foremost was the province of Buenos Aires, which included the city itself and spread south to include part of the Pampas. Far to the west on the arid, sunny slopes along the foot of the Andes was another Argentina, the towns of Córdoba, Salta, and Tucumán. During the colonial era these cities had developed and prospered along the trail from the Spanish center in Lima to the developing colonies in Chile. But as the commerce had risen in Buenos Aires, their importance had dwindled. Third was the region north and west of Buenos Aires, focusing on the city of Santa Fe, which dominated much of the upper Río de la Plata. Last and perhaps most important was the Pampas, the spiritual and geographical heart of the country, whose *estancieros* and gauchos would always be suspicious of the well-dressed men of the cities who traveled so much on foot. Of Patagonia, people thought not at all.

During the ten years following independence, civil wars raged between Buenos Aires and the *caudillos* of the separate provinces. They fought mainly over the issue of unifying into a nation under a strong central government in Buenos Aires or staying a federation, where local leaders could remain powerful. For better or worse, Rosas succeeded in uniting Argentina into a country. Though his dictatorship was still two years in the future, he had already taken his first step toward gaining absolute power.

Born of a good family in Buenos Aires, Rosas had nonetheless grown up a child of the Pampas. When very young, he went to live on one of his father's *estancias*. He was in truth raised on horseback, living and learning of life as a gaucho and excelling in the skills that the gauchos so admired. Although he never fought during the war of independence, Rosas had joined the militia in 1813 and remained in it ever since, fighting regional wars against the *caudillos* and the ever more numerous battles against the Indians. Eventually he became a wealthy man, an owner of *estancias,* salting factories, and ships. But the source of a *caudillo*'s power was his following; Rosas had the unswerving faith of the Pampas' gauchos, and with them he swept into his first position of formal leadership.

In 1828 the Argentine Confederation was falling apart. Aside from what design Rosas may have had then on central power, the anarchy was hurting business. One day he rode into Buenos Aires, followed by a galloping band of gauchos bent on restoring order, and ended up Buenos Aires' governor for the next three years.

The year before Darwin and Rosas met, he had stepped down from the governorship, leaving his wife behind to start a movement that would pave the way for his return to power. He went to the Pampas to fight his own private war against the Indians. His army of gauchos and friendly Indians had recently set up a permanent camp near the Río Colorado.

It consisted of a square formed by waggons, artillery, straw huts, &c. The soldiers were nearly all cavalry; and I should think such a villanous, banditti-like army was never before collected together. The greater number of men were of a mixed breed, between Negro, Indian, and Spaniard. I know not the reason, but men of such origin seldom have a good expression. . . .

Darwin intended to obtain a passport to travel through the territory under the control of Rosas' army. After a brief interview with Rosas' secretary, who questioned him closely about what apparently seemed a mysterious mission, Darwin settled down for two days at a rundown rancho owned by an old Spaniard. With the land surrounded by swamp, Darwin found little to do. But with characteristic curiosity he observed the families of the Indians allied with Rosas that came to buy articles at the rancho.

The men were a tall, fine race, yet it was afterwards easy to see in the Fuegian savage the same countenance rendered hideous by cold, want of food, and less civilization. . . . Among the young women or chinas, some deserve to be called even beautiful. Their hair was coarse, but bright and black; and they wore it in two plaits hanging down to the waist. They had a high colour, and eyes that glistened with brilliancy; their legs, feet, and arms were small and elegantly formed; their ankles, and sometimes their waists, were ornamented by broad bracelets of blue beads. . . . A mother with one or two daughters would often come to our rancho, mounted on the same horse. They ride like men, but with their knees tucked up much higher. This habit, perhaps, arises from their being accustomed, when travelling to ride the loaded horses. The duty of the women is to load and unload the horses; to make the tents for the night; in short to be, like the wives of all savages, useful slaves. The men fight, hunt, take care of the horses, and make the riding gear. One of their chief indoor occupations is to knock two stones together till they become round, in order to make the bolas. With this important weapon the Indian catches his game, and also his horse, which roams free over the plain. In fighting, his first attempt is to throw down the horse of his adversary with the bolas, and when entangled by the fall to kill him with the chuzo. If the balls only catch the neck or body of an animal, they are often carried away and lost. As the making the stones round is the labour of two days, the manufacture of the balls is a very common employment. Several of the men and women had their faces painted red. . . . Their chief pride consists in having everything made of silver; I have seen a cacique with his spurs, stirrups, handle of his knife, and bridle made of this metal. . . .

Having no particular affection for the English, who Rosas believed had kept Banda Oriental out of the Argentine Empire for good, the general was perhaps intrigued by the *naturalista* and asked to see Darwin. In the light of history it was an interview Darwin was later glad of. Of Rosas, he wrote:

He is a man of an extraordinary character, and has a most predominant influence in the country. . . . He is said to be the owner of seventy-four square leagues of land, and to have about three hundred thousand head of cattle. His estates are admirably managed, and are far more productive of corn than those of others. He first gained his celebrity by his laws for his own estancias, and by disciplining several hundred men, so as to resist with success the attacks of the Indians. There are many stories current about the rigid manner in which his laws were enforced. One of these was, that no man, on penalty of being put into the stocks, should carry his knife on a Sunday: this being the principal day for gambling and drinking, many quarrels arose, which from the general manner of fighting with the knife often proved fatal. One Sunday the Governor came in great form to pay the estancia a visit, and General Rosas in his hurry, walked out to receive him with his knife, as usual, stuck in his belt. The steward touched his arm, and reminded him of the law; upon which turning to the Governor, he said he was extremely sorry, but that he must go into the stocks, and that till let out, he possessed no power even in his own house. After a little time the steward was persuaded to open the stocks, and to let him out, but no sooner was this done, then he turned to the steward and said, "You now have broken the laws, so you must take my place in the stocks." Such actions as these delighted the Gauchos, who all possess high notions of their own equality and dignity.

General Rosas is also a perfect horseman—an accomplishment of no small consequence in a country where an assembled army elected its general by the following trial: A troop of unbroken horses being driven into a corral, were let out through a gateway, above which was a crossbar: it was agreed whoever should drop from the bar on one of these wild animals, as it rushed out, and should be able, without saddle or bridle, not only to ride it, but also to bring it back to the door of the corral, should be their general. . . . This extraordinary feat has also been performed by Rosas.

By these means, and by conforming to the dress and habits of the Gauchos, he has obtained an unbounded popularity in the country, and in consequence a despotic power. . . .

The meeting between Darwin and Rosas was brief. Darwin found the general's conversation enthusiastic, sensible but grave; his manner was obliging, but his appearance startling. For all his reputation and feats of prowess, Darwin must have expected something other than the bright-blue-eyed man whose reddish-brown hair was worn with long side-whiskers. But the interview passed without a smile. When it was finished, Darwin had received a passport and an order for horses to be supplied at the government posthouses that spanned the area from the Río Colorado to Buenos Aires, spaced a day's ride apart across the Pampas. That night Darwin wrote in his diary that he was altogether pleased with the interview. "He is worth seeing, as being decidedly the most prominent character in S. America." The next morning Darwin's party left for Bahía Blanca, arriving there two days later.

To Darwin's eye Bahía Blanca scarcely deserved to be called a village. At Rosas' order the site had been occupied only four years before; it consisted of a few houses for the troops surrounded by a wall and a deep ditch. The territory outside the walls belonged as much to the Indians as to the soldiers. The part of the bay where Darwin was to meet the *Beagle* was another twenty-five miles away, and the guide Darwin rode with had been attacked and wounded by Indians only two months before. Upon reaching the cliffs overlooking the bay, Darwin found the bay empty, the horizon unbroken by sail. Another trip two days later had the same result.

During Darwin's stay at Bahía Blanca he was able to add more fossil hunting to his earlier searches. But the village was in a constant state of excitement over news and rumors of battles with the Indians. One day the talk was about soldiers who had been murdered at one of the posts along the line to Buenos Aires. The next day 300 men arrived from the Río Colorado to track down the Indians, with orders to follow them to Chile if necessary. They camped overnight at Bahía Blanca, and their bivouac was the most savage and wild thing that Darwin had ever seen. Most of the soldiers were *mansos,* so-called tame Indians, but there was nothing civilized about their stay at the village. "Some drank till they were intoxicated;

others swallowed the steaming blood of the cattle slaughtered for their suppers. . . ."

The next morning they left as quickly as they had come. Darwin heard later that they had ridden 300 miles through unknown country, following the track of the Indians but never finding them. "As long as there is a little water," wrote Darwin, "these men would penetrate to the end of the world."

To Darwin, the war seemed a brutal waste. Rosas' strategy was to drive the Indians, if possible, to some central place, killing the stragglers he ran across. He was prepared to spend three years, if need be, trying to maneuver the Indians into situations where his armies, in alliance with the Chileans, could attack en masse. Darwin predicted that if Rosas were successful, there would not be a wild Indian left north of the Río Negro. Brutality was returned in kind by the Indians, who unmercifully tortured those soldiers unfortunate enough to be taken alive. One illustration serves to point out the cruelty of the campaign:

Some Indians, who had been taken prisoners, gave information of a tribe living north of the Colorado. Two hundred soldiers were sent; and they first discovered the Indians by a cloud of dust from their horses' feet, as they chanced to be travelling. The country was mountainous and wild, and it must have been far in the interior, for the Cordillera were in sight. The Indians, men, women, and children, were about one hundred and ten in number, and they were nearly all taken or killed, for the soldiers sabre every man. The Indians are now so terrified that they offer no resistance in a body, but each flies, neglecting even his wife and children; but when overtaken, like wild animals, they fight against any number to the last moment. One dying Indian seized with his teeth the thumb of his adversary, and allowed his own eye to be forced out sooner than relinquish his hold. Another, who was wounded, feigned death, keeping a knife ready to strike one more fatal blow. My informer said, when he was pursuing an Indian, the man cried out for mercy, at the same time that he was covertly loosing the bolas from his waist, meaning to whirl it round his head and so strike his pursuer. "I however struck him with my sabre to the ground, and then got off my horse, and cut his throat with my knife." This is a dark picture; but how much more shocking is the unquestionable fact, that all the women who appear above twenty years old are massacred in cold blood! When I exclaimed that this appeared rather inhuman, he answered, "Why, what can be done? they breed so!"

Every one here is fully convinced that this is the most just war, because it is against barbarians. Who would believe in this age that such atrocities could be committed in a Christian civilized country? The children of the Indians are saved, to be sold or given away as servants, or rather slaves for as long a time as the owners can make them believe themselves slaves. . . .

The logical escape of the Indians, barred by the Andes on the west, was south across the Río Negro into barren Patagonia. But Rosas' objective was extermination, not shifting the Indians to less important lands. With characteristic shewdness he made a treaty with the Tehuelches, the most notherly tribe of Patagonia, to this effect:

. . . Rosas pays them so much to slaughter every Indian who passes to the south of the river, but if they fail in so doing, they themselves are to be exterminated. The war is waged chiefly against the Indians near the Cordillera; for many of the tribes on this eastern side are fighting with Rosas. The general, however, like Lord Chesterfield, thinking that his friends may in a future day become his enemies, always places them in the front ranks, so that their numbers may be thinned.

Though Darwin's descriptions of the bloodshed were matter-of-fact, the deterioration of the Indians' tribal life in the act of resisting was, for him, a melancholy sight. One senses Darwin's sympathy with the Indians in such passages as this, written several weeks later:

I heard also some account of an engagement which took place, a few weeks previously to the one mentioned, at Chole-chel. This is a very important station on account of being a pass for horses; and it was, in consequence, for some time the headquarters of a division of the army. When the troops first arrived there they found a tribe of Indians, of whom they killed twenty or thirty. The cacique escaped in a manner which astonished everyone. The chief Indians always have one or two picked horses, which they keep ready for any urgent occasion. On one of these, an old white horse, the cacique sprung, taking with him his little son. The horse had neither saddle nor bridle. To avoid the shots, the Indian rode in the peculiar method of his nation; namely, with an arm round the horse's neck, and one leg only on its back. Thus hanging on one side he was seen patting the horse's head, and talking to him. The pursuers urged every effort in the chace; the Commandant three times changed his horse, but all in vain. The old Indian father and his son escaped, and were free. . . .

The *Beagle* arrived at Bahía Blanca August 24, 1833. A week later it sailed north for the Plata, leaving Darwin behind. Despite the danger from Indians, he had decided to travel the 400 miles to Buenos Aires by land.

8

Mysterious Fossils
SEPTEMBER, 1833 —DECEMBER, 1833

THE posthouses left behind by Rosas as he moved his army south across the Pampas were rudely built shacks, the horses and corral protected by a few soldiers. Many of the *estancias* had been abandoned since the renewed campaigns of the Indians to rid the land of invaders, and the posthouses for Rosas' couriers and travelers in his favor provided at least a measure of protection.

Even with the posthouses, Darwin and his gaucho guide took fourteen days to travel the 400 miles to Buenos Aires. A messenger for Rosas would have made it in less time. But as usual, Indians or no, Darwin took his time, riding at a leisurely pace and pausing when he found something worth his attention. Darwin felt that few regions had been so changed by man as the Pampas.

The countless herds of horses, cattle, and sheep, not only have altered the whole aspect of the vegetation, but they have almost banished the guanaco, deer, and ostrich. Numberless other changes must likewise have taken place; the wild pig in some parts probably replaces the pecarri; packs of wild dogs may be heard howling on the wooded banks of the less frequented streams; and the common cat, altered into a large and fierce animal, inhabits rocky hills. . . .

At each of the posthouses Darwin found the soldiers hospitable, but their lonely and dangerous life seemed miserable. Everywhere their talk was only of Rosas and the war against the Indians. On September 15, the sixth day of the journey, they passed the posthouse where the soldiers had been murdered while Darwin was at Bahía Blanca. On the eighteenth, only two days' ride from Buenos Aires, they stayed at one of the great *estancias* of Rosas. Until then Darwin had lived like a gaucho, eating meat day after day, smoking the harsh black cigars, and always sipping the cup of maté tea at day's end.

By midday of the 20th, Darwin had arrived in Buenos Aires. Several days before, the *Beagle* had arrived at Montevideo. The *Adventure*'s refitting was still not completed, and FitzRoy had finishing touches to add to the charts of the Plata and the Argentine coast. All of this would delay their departure, and FitzRoy thoughtfully sent Sims Covington to Buenos Aires to inform Darwin of the delay. Hearing the news, Darwin decided to take advantage of the time ashore.

Sending Covington to a nearby *estancia* to skin and stuff a collection of birds, Darwin planned to head for the city of Santa Fe, 300 miles to the north, just past the northern extremity of the Pampas on the Río Paraná. Because of the thick river deposits found there, this was country with a good likelihood of fossils.

Darwin had found his first fossil animal a little more than a year before. In the sandy beach at Punta Alta, north of Bahía Blanca, Darwin uncovered parts of a megatherium, a large extinct cousin of the armadillo. Thinking at first it was a part of a living species, he planned to send the bones and shell to Henslow at first chance.

The significance of fossils was sketchily understood by geologists of Darwin's time. Fossils had been known for centuries, particularly fossil seashells, which had been discovered in many places in Europe—in quarries, road cuts, and most noticeably, embedded in the rock of many of Europe's mountains.

The geologists of the seventeenth century could barely explain them. They hypothesized that perhaps fossils had never been alive, that they were merely jokes of nature, bearing accidental resemblance to living things.

The catastrophists had a more refined view, for by the nineteenth century, attention had been focused on the fossil bones of animals, particularly the mammoth quadrupeds that once had roamed the earth. The catastrophists said that fossils were the records of past life which had been snuffed out by one of the Creator's deluges. Seashells embedded at high altitudes meant only that the deluge had been a truly great one, for only water could rise that high. The idea that mountains could have been uplifted from sea level was unthought of. After the deluge, the Creator put upon the earth a whole new set of beings. Man and the present species of plants and animals were thought to date only from the Great Deluge of the Bible.

The idea of fossils as a record of past life was closer to the truth than the catastrophists realized. Yet the reason for extinct species was thought to be the direct action of a divine master planner. That present life could have descended from former extinct species by evolution was an unsatisfactory explanation for most naturalists. FitzRoy had a still more simple answer to explain the fossil bones found by Darwin. They were merely those unfortunate animals that were unable to get aboard Noah's Ark.

The catastrophists' theory of new species created after each flood could not explain why many of the fossils that Darwin discovered were similar to living species. There was no clear reason for new species to resemble former creations. Yet the similarity had been noticed, and Darwin was not the first to realize it. Lyell had hinted that existing species had a close relation to extinct species, although in *Principles of Geology* he never developed the idea of descent by evolution.

Discovering the megatherium, so obviously similar to the armadillo, and finding other fossils similar to living species led Darwin to ask, again and again: why the similarity? Why were extinct species so much like ones that he found living in nearly the same location? In his mind the theories did not explain the facts—the facts that he had dug from the earth with his own hands.

Of course, Darwin found many other fossils far removed from living species. Also at Punta Alta he had found the remains of a toxodon and a scelidotherium. The latter, he noted, must once have been as big as a rhinoceros. He found the bones of a mylodon, the great vegetarian pachyderm that lived millions of years ago and foraged for food by pulling down trees with its claws while resting on its massive tail and hind feet. At Santa Fe his good luck at fossil finding continued.

Darwin took a week to make arrangements for the trip to Santa Fe, and it wasn't until the twenty-seventh that he and his guides were able to set off. The country was flat, and they made good time. By September 30 they had passed through the village of Rosario, perched on the high banks overlooking the Río Paraná. Following the river, they continued north. On October 1 they crossed one of the tributaries of the Paraná, the Río Tercero, one of many rivers that flow eastward from the Andes.

Here Darwin spent a day searching for fossil bones. In addition to the tooth of a toxodon, he found two immense skeletons embedded in the riverbank. They were so completely decayed he was able to take only the fragments of a tooth. Still, this was enough for him to identify the remains as those of a mastodon. Darwin was told that the people nearby had long known of the bones' location and that everyone had wondered how they could have gotten there. The consensus was that these mammoth anteced-ents of the elephant had once, like gophers, burrowed into the ground.

From the Río Tercero they passed through the village of Corunda into Indian country once again. With the return of danger his guides became alert and watchful. Wrote Darwin:

From this point to St. Fé the road is not very safe. The western side of the Parana northward, ceases to be inhabited; and hence the Indians sometimes come down thus far, and waylay travellers. . . . We passed some houses that had been ransacked and since deserted; we saw also a spectacle, which my guides viewed with high satisfaction; it was the skeleton of an Indian with the dried skin hanging on the bones, suspended to the branch of a tree.

Darwin arrived at Santa Fe the morning of October 2.

St. Fé is a quiet little town, and is kept clean and in good order. The governor, Lopez, was a common soldier at the time of the revolution; but has now been seventeen years in power. This stability of government is owing to his tyrannical habits; for tyranny seems as yet better adapted to these countries than republicanism. The governor's favourite occupation is hunting Indians: a short time since he slaughtered forty-eight, and sold the children at the rate of three or four pounds apiece.

The strain of two months' travel overtook Darwin at Santa Fe, however, and he spent two days with fever and a headache. The jovial old woman who attended him was convinced that his only road to health was to use one of the local remedies for such sicknesses. Darwin termed the cures odd.

A common practice is, to bind an orange-leaf or a bit of black plaster to each temple: and a still more general plan is, to split a bean into halves, moisten them, and place one on each temple, where they will easily adhere. It is not thought proper ever to remove the beans or the plaster, but to allow them to drop off; and sometimes if a man with patches on his head, is asked, what is the matter? he will answer, "I had a headach the day before yesterday. . . ."

By whichever method, Darwin was cured by October 5. He then crossed the Paraná into the province of Entre Ríos, where he spent a week studying geology. Here he found more fossils. One was "the osseous armour of a gigantic armadillo-like animal, the inside of which, when the earth was removed, was like a great cauldron." He also found more remains of both a toxodon and mastodon, as well as those of a horse. Though intending to push on farther, by the twelfth he was ill again and decided to return to Buenos Aires.

Instead of by horseback —he had in two months already traveled more than eight hundred miles —he chose a balandra, one of the large barges that navigated leisurely down the Paraná. The trip took a week, more than enough leisure for Darwin. By the time they neared Buenos Aires, he was anxious to get back to the *Beagle*.

Thinking that the ship must surely be preparing to leave the Plata, Darwin left the balandra at Las Conchas, determined to take a faster overland route to Buenos Aires, where he could make arrangements for transport to Montevideo. Landing at Las Conchas, he was dismayed to hear that in the brief time he had been gone, revolution had broken out in Buenos Aires. The city was blockaded.

To reach the *Beagle,* he had to get into the city. Finally getting permission from a local commandant, Darwin saw the commander of the rebels controlling the territory between Las Conchas and Buenos Aires.

My reception at the encampment was quite civil, but I was told it was impossible that I could be allowed to enter the city.... Having mentioned, however, General Rosas's obliging kindness to me when at the Colorado, magic itself could not have altered circumstances quicker. ...

In Buenos Aires, Darwin described the revolution which had nearly separated him from the *Beagle.* It is a good example of the type which was common in the countries near the Plata at the time:

This revolution was supported by scarcely any pretext of grievances. . . . In this case, a party of men—who, being attached to Rosas, were disgusted with the governor Balcarce— to the number of seventy left the city, and with the cry of Rosas the whole country took arms. The city was then blockaded, no provisions, cattle or horses, were allowed to enter; besides this, there was only a little skirmishing, and a few men daily killed. The outside party well knew that by stopping the supply of meat they would certainly be victorious. General Rosas could not have known of this rising; but it appears to be quite consonant with the plans of his party. A year ago he was elected governor, but he refused it, unless the Sala would also confer on him extraordinary powers. This was refused, and since then his party have shown that no other governor can keep his place. The warfare on both sides was avowedly protracted till it was possible to hear from Rosas. A note arrived a few days after I left Buenos Ayres, which stated that the General disapproved of peace having been broken, but that he thought the outside party had justice on their side. On the bare reception of this, the Governor, ministers, and part of the military, to the number of some hundreds, fled from the city. The rebels entered, elected a new governor, and were paid for their services to the number of 5,500 men. From these proceedings, it was clear that Rosas ultimately would become the dictator: to the term king, the people in this, as in other republics, have a particular dislike. . . .

On arriving in Montevideo, Darwin found the *Beagle* still unready to sail. There was time for one more brief trip, this time through the former Portuguese colony at Colonia, then north to the small town of Mercedes near the Río Uruguay. This was his last opportunity to study the regions near the Plata and his last chance to probe the deep beds of the Pampas for fossils.

I believe a straight line drawn in any direction through the Pampas would cut through some skeletons or bones. Besides those which I found during my short excursions, I heard of many others, and the origin of such names as "the stream of the animal," "the hill of the giant," is obvious. At other times I heard of the marvellous property of certain rivers, which had the power of changing small bones into large; or, as some maintained, the bones themselves grew. As far as I am aware, not one of these animals perished, as was formerly supposed, in the marshes or muddy river-beds of the present land, but their bones have been exposed by the streams intersecting the . . . deposit in which they were originally embedded. We may conclude that the whole area of the Pampas is one wide sepulchre of these extinct quadrupeds.

On November 28 he was back in Montevideo, and on December 6, 1833, the *Beagle* sailed from the Río de la Plata, "never again to enter its muddy stream."

Concerned as Darwin was about plants and animals living and extinct, he had been equally impressed by the people of the Plata. He summarized his observations thus:

During the last six months I have had an opportunity of seeing a little of the character of the inhabitants of these provinces. The Gauchos, or countrymen, are very superior to those who reside in the towns. The Gaucho is invariably most obliging, polite, and hospitable: I did not meet with even one instance of rudeness or inhospitality. He is modest, both respecting himself and country, but at the same time a spirited, bold fellow. On the other hand, many robberies are committed, and there is much bloodshed: the habit of constantly wearing the knife is the chief cause of the latter. It is lamentable to hear how many lives are lost in trifling quarrels. In fighting, each party tries to mark the face of his adversary by slashing his nose or eyes; as is often attested by deep and horrid-looking scars. Robberies are a natural consequence of universal gambling, much drinking, and extreme indolence. At Mercedes I asked two men why they did not work. One gravely said the days were too long; the other that he was too poor. The number of horses and the profusion of food are the destruction of all industry. Moreover, there are so many feast-days; and again, nothing can succeed without it be begun when the moon is on the increase; so that half the month is lost from these two causes.

Police and justice are quite inefficient. If a man who is poor commits murder and is taken, he will be imprisoned, and perhaps even shot; but if he is rich and has friends, he may rely on it no very severe consequence will ensue. It is curious that the most respectable inhabitants of the country invariably assist a murderer to escape: they seem to think that the individual sins against the government, and not against the people. A traveller has no protection besides his fire-arms; and the constant habit of carrying them is the main check to more frequent robberies.

The character of the higher and more educated classes who reside in the towns, partakes, but perhaps in a lesser degree, of the good parts of the Gaucho, but is, I fear, stained by many vices of which he is free: Sensuality, mockery of all religion, and the grossest corruption, are far from uncommon. Nearly every public officer can be bribed. The head man in the post-office sold forged government franks. The governor and prime minister openly combined to plunder the state. Justice, where gold came into play, was hardly expected by any one. . . . With this entire want of principle in many of the leading men, with the country full of ill-paid turbulent officers, the people yet hope that a democratic form of government can succeed!

On first entering society in these countries, two or three features strike one as particularly remarkable. The polite and dignified manners pervading every rank of life, the excellent taste displayed by the women in their dresses, and the equality among all ranks. At the Rio Colorado some men who kept the humblest shops used to dine with General Rosas. . . . Many officers in the army can neither read nor write, yet all meet in society as equals. . . .

When speaking of these countries, the manner in which they have been brought up by their unnatural parent, Spain, should always be borne in mind. On the whole, perhaps, more credit is due for what has been done, than blame for that which may be deficient. It is impossible to doubt but that the extreme liberalism of these countries must ultimately lead to good results. The very general toleration of foreign religions, the regard paid to the means of education, the freedom of the press, the facilities offered to all foreigners, and especially, as I am bound to add, to every one professing the humblest pretensions to science, should be recollected with gratitude by those who have visited Spanish South America.

9

Patagonia

DECEMBER, 1833—JUNE, 1834

FOR DARWIN, Patagonia should have been a total loss. Plants and animals were meager in number. He had an idea of what to expect after glimpsing Patagonia's northern fringes when he had followed the Río Negro to the village of El Carmen the previous August. He portrayed the plant life there as wretched in the extreme: "The vegetation is scanty; and although there are bushes of many kinds, all are armed with formidable thorns, which seem to warn the stranger not to enter on these inhospitable regions."

It was an apt description. South of the Pampas and east of the Andes the plateau of Patagonia had been bypassed almost completely by civilized man. It was little more than a cool desert. Animals were as sparse as plant life —a few insects, predominately the drought-loving scorpion, carrion hawks, a few lizards, and a surprising number of rodents. Added to this was only the long-necked guanaco, the elegant and graceful cousin of the llama. That Patagonia was biologically disappointing was no surprise for Darwin. The surprise came years later, when he found that he remembered its seemingly monotonous landscape as one of the most unforgettable of the voyage.

In calling up images of the past, I find that the plains of Patagonia frequently cross before my eyes; yet these plains are pronounced by all wretched and useless. They can be described only by negative characters; without habitations, without water, without trees, without mountains, they support merely a few dwarf plants. Why then, and the case is not peculiar to myself, have these arid wastes taken so firm a hold on my memory? Why have not the still more level, the greener and more fertile Pampas, which are serviceable to mankind, produced an equal impression? I can scarcely analyze these feelings: but it must be partly owing to the free scope given to the imagination. The plains of Patagonia are boundless, for they are scarcely passable, and hence unknown: they bear the stamp of having lasted, as they are now, for ages, and there appears no limit to their duration through future time. . . . who would not look at these last boundaries to man's knowledge with deep but ill-defined sensations?

The *Beagle* landed at the deserted Spanish settlement named Puerto Deseado —Port Desire —two days before Christmas 1834, seventeen days after leaving the mouth of the Plata. While FitzRoy surveyed the harbor and adjacent land, searching mainly for watering sites, Darwin took long walks alone over the desolate terrain. Perhaps it was "the free scope given the imagination" that spurred him to speculate more freely now, or maybe it was the two years of hard experience in the field.

Along the coast from the Plata south, he had found the remains of marine animals—species still existing—embedded in deposits far above sea level. These shells indicated to Darwin that portions of the coast had emerged above the sea during a recent era of geologic time. Now far inland from Puerto Deseado, he discovered additional great beds of seashells, dry and sun-bleached from years of exposure to the elements. Darwin began to feel that the whole of Patagonia may have once been beneath the sea. Could the emergence of the entire Patagonian plateau have been the result of one gigantic catastrophe? Perhaps, but it appeared doubtful. Though his powers of observation were sharper than ever, Darwin felt weak and theoretically underequipped for hypothesis in geology. Given the theories of the time, he seemed to end up with more questions than explanations. In a letter to Henslow written three months later, he pleaded for help to throw light on some of his questions: "I have no books which tell me much, and what they do I cannot apply. . . ." Preoccupied with geology, Darwin nearly missed a discovery at Puerto Deseado which added a piece to the mosaic that eventually became his theory of evolution.

Like the unexplained similarity between extinct and living species, the theories gave little reason why species in adjacent regions should differ, yet have so many similarities. If the adjacent regions were separated by a barrier, such as a mountain range or a river, the reason for separate species was understandable. But the Pampas and Patagonia were not separated by such barriers. Wouldn't it have been easier, he questioned, for the Creator to have designed just one model and distributed it widely over both regions? So it was with the South American ostrich, or rhea.

At the Río Negro a few months before, Darwin had heard the gauchos talking of a rare kind of ostrich, smaller than and differently feathered from the common ostrich. At a distance the gauchos could tell the difference, and the smaller one was more easily brought down by the bolas. Farther south of the Río Negro, in Patagonia, they were said to be common.

At Puerto Deseado a crew member assigned the task of searching out dinner shot an ostrich which looked to Darwin to be "a not full-grown bird of the common sort." It was cooked, served, and nearly eaten when Darwin's mind clicked. They were dining on the rare ostrich. "Fortunately," wrote Darwin, "the head, neck, legs, wings, many of the larger feathers, and a large part of the skin, had been preserved; and from these a very nearly perfect specimen has been put together." It was sent, like so many others of his discoveries, back to England to be analyzed by experts. Later study and description found it was indeed a new species, promptly named *Rhea Darwini.*

In such desolate country it was no wonder to Darwin that the Spanish had abandoned Puerto Deseado. With the survey finished, the *Beagle,* too, deserted the arid site and pushed south to Port St. Julien, 110 miles south, in similar country but if anything, Darwin noted, "rather more sterile." Here the work was the same. For FitzRoy it was a chart of the harbor and a search for possible sources of water. For Darwin it was geology, work with hammer and compass, and a little speculation.

Near Port St. Julien his hammer uncovered another fossil, the bones of "a remarkable quadruped, fully as large as a camel," that, because of its long neck, seemed to be related to the guanaco. It was the same disturbing problem again: Why should extinct species be so similar to living ones? Whatever he thought might be the explanation to the problem, he noted in his journal merely that his observations were "interesting facts." For the time he was content not to hypothesize but to remain the "lions' provider."

Eight days spent at Port St. Julien brought the survey of the coast of Patagonia near an end. Only the port and harbor of Río Santa Cruz farther south remained. It had been almost a year and a half, however, since FitzRoy had returned the three Fuegians, and he felt it was time to see how they had fared as well as to finish the survey of Tierra del Fuego. It was south again for the *Beagle*. Two and a half months later —on April 6, 1834 —Darwin wrote to his sister Catherine from the Falkland Islands, describing what happened:

After visiting some of the southern islands, we beat up through the magnificent scenery of the Beagle Channel to Jemmy Button's country. We could hardly recognise poor Jemmy. Instead of the clean, well-dressed stout lad we left him, we found him a naked, thin, squalid savage. York and Fuegia had moved to their own country some months ago, the former having stolen all Jemmy's clothes. Now he had nothing except a bit of blanket round his waist. Poor Jemmy was glad to see us, and, with his usual good feeling, brought several presents (otter-skins, which are most valuable to themselves) for his old friends. The Captain offered to take him to England, but this, to our surprise, he at once refused. In the evening his young wife came alongside and showed us the reason. He was quite contented. Last year, in the height of his indignation, he said "his country people no *sabe* nothing—damned fools—" now they were very good people, with *too* much to eat, and all the luxuries of life. Jemmy and his wife paddled away in their canoe loaded with presents, and very happy. The most curious thing is, that Jemmy, instead of recovering his own language, has taught all his friends a little English. "J. Button's canoe" and "Jemmy's wife come," "Give me knife," &c., was said by several of them.

Returning to the Falkland Islands after FitzRoy's disappointing view of Jemmy, they found that since they had left, the gauchos had staged an uprising against the English and had murdered the British officer and as many other Britishers as they could catch. A party of marines left by a British man-of-war caught the murderers, "there now being as many prisoners as inhabitants."

Darwin took a brief four-day ride around East Island, enduring a continuous gale accompanied by hail and snow. The weather added to the dreariness of the place, Darwin remaining wet and uncomfortable the whole time. "Sleeping out at night was too miserable work to endure it for all the rocks in South America," he remarked. A few days later, leaving the *Adventure* behind to complete the chart and survey of the Falklands, the *Beagle* headed for the Río Santa Cruz. The *Beagle* had grazed a rock near Puerto Deseado and torn some copper sheathing loose from the hull. In addition to finishing the work on the east coast, FitzRoy wanted to repair the *Beagle*. Then they would meet the *Adventure* at Port Famine in Tierra del Fuego and sail on together to the Pacific. Darwin believed there was a chance of the *Beagle*'s having to return to the frozen and bitter southern lands, but he wrote, "If any one catches me there again, I will give him leave to hang me up as a scarecrow for all future naturalists. . . ."

Before the days of ship-lifting cranes and drydocks, the standard method for having a look at a ship's bottom was called careening. FitzRoy intended to careen the *Beagle* in the broad bay at the mouth of the Río Santa Cruz. At high tide the *Beagle* was run firm aground on a flat, sandy beach, and all hands were put ashore. Then as the tide receded, the *Beagle* gently heeled over on her side. At low tide almost the entire underside of the *Beagle* was visible, exposing the few feet of false keel that had been ripped away when the *Beagle* grazed the underwater rock. It was a simple repair job, and by the next high tide the *Beagle* had slowly righted herself and floated free to be anchored offshore while FitzRoy led his expedition up the Santa Cruz. Its survey had been begun six years before by Captain Pringle Stokes, the ill-fated former commander of the *Beagle*. Stokes had intended to follow the river, which slices across the entire lower Patagonia plateau, to its headwaters in the Andes. It was until then unexplored land, wandered over only by scattered tribes of Indians. But the river's current was

The *Beagle* careened near the Río Santa Cruz.

strong, the going slower than he had expected. Thirty miles upstream, shortage of provisions had forced Stokes' party to turn back. The work that Stokes had begun FitzRoy was determined to finish, climbing if possible to the crest of the Andes.

On April 18, 1834, three whaleboats and twenty-five men, Darwin included, set off with three weeks' provisions up the Santa Cruz. Darwin describes the manner in which they worked the heavy boats upstream:

Against so strong a current it was, of course, quite impossible to row or sail: consequently the three boats were fastened together head and stern, two hands left in each, and the rest came on shore to track. As the general arrangements made by Captain FitzRoy were very good for facilitating the work of all, and as all had a share in it, I will describe the system. The party, including everyone, was divided into two spells, each of which hauled at the tracking line alternately for an hour and a half. The officers of each boat lived with, ate the same food, and slept in the same tent with their crew, so that each boat was quite independent of the others. After sunset the first level spot where any bushes were growing, was chosen for our night's lodging. Each of the crew took it in turns to be cook. Immediately the boat was hauled up, the cook made his fire; two others pitched the tent; the coxswain handed the things out of the boat; the rest carried them up to the tents and collected firewood. By this order, in half an hour everything was ready for the night. A watch of two men and an officer was always kept, whose duty it was to look after the boats, keep up the fire, and guard against Indians. Each in the party had his one hour every night.

In this manner they made their way along the river, mile after tedious mile, sometimes averaging 10 miles a day, sometimes a little more. By the third day of the trip they had passed the point where Stokes had turned back and later crossed fresh tracks of Indians near the river. If uninteresting sameness can be striking, this alone was the mark of Patagonia's character for Darwin: "The level plains of arid shingle support the same stunted and dwarf plants; and in the valleys the same thorn-bearing bushes grow. Everywhere we see the same birds and insects. . . . The curse of sterility is on the land."

So it continued for the next week, Darwin making his observations on geology, jotting them in his pocket notebooks between stints of lugging away at the whaleboats as one of the crew. On April 29, the eleventh day of the trek, they saw the summits of the Andes "peeping through their dusty envelope of clouds." This far upstream, the river's course had narrowed, the current sweeping faster along the channel. FitzRoy estimated its speed at 6 knots, and maneuvering the boats against the swiftness was more difficult now —and dangerous.

They had, in addition, made poorer time than FitzRoy had hoped for, and he already had resorted to half rations of bread. Finally the decision became apparent. With the front ranges of the Andes looming ahead of them, 140 miles from their beginning, FitzRoy decided to take the boats no farther. At this point they were closer to the Pacific than to the Atlantic. But the time needed to work the boats higher, measured against the shortage of food, became too costly a gamble.

On May 5 they began their return trip, and in three days, moving with the current, they easily swept past country they had covered so painfully only days before. By May 8 they were back aboard the *Beagle.* Much of the expedition had been through unexplored land. But falling short of the Andes had left FitzRoy and the crew disappointed. For Darwin, however, it had been a magnificent opportunity to see a cross section of the entire Patagonian plateau. As for the Andes, as soon as they rendezvoused with the *Adventure,* he would have a look at them from the other side.

It was late May by the time the *Beagle* reentered the Strait of Magellan for what all hands hoped would be a one-way passage. The land near the eastern entrance, continuing for nearly 100 miles, reminded Darwin of the low plains of Patagonia. Then past Cape Negro the typical landscape of Tierra del Fuego began —the dense, dull evergreen forests, covering mountains that rise from the water's edge to lose their snowy crests in the ever-present gray mists.

Port Famine was roughly midway along the Strait of Magellan. The *Beagle* arrived to find the Fuegians who lived nearby up to their typical tricks. During the first expedition their troublesome willingness to plunder had been halted when a red rocket was sent to burst high above their village one night. The next day the Indians were gone. This time, to discourage an interest in whale-boats and instruments, musket balls were fired through the treetops. The result was the same. It was necessary, for the *Beagle* spent a long week waiting for the *Adventure.*

Finally the ship arrived and, joined by the *Beagle,* sailed out of Port Famine on June 8. The next day the ship passed the glacier-carved coast and beneath Mount Sarmiento, one of Tierra del Fuego's highest peaks. Finding no anchorage that night, the *Beagle* hove to and stood off for fourteen hours. In these dangerous waters the *Beagle* sailed only with the daylight. Instead of leaving the strait by its usual exit, FitzRoy chose the recently discovered Magdallen Channel, which brought them into the Pacific just north of a large bleak piece of land appropriately named Desolation Island. On the morning of the tenth they made their way into the Pacific. Wrote Darwin:

We passed out between the East and West Furies; and a little farther northward there are so many breakers that the sea is called the Milky Way. One sight of such a coast is enough to make a landsman dream for a week about shipwrecks, peril, and death; and with this sight we bade farewell forever to Tierra del Fuego.

10

The Happy Life
JUNE, 1834—APRIL, 1835

THE WEST coast of South America had never brought much luck to the *Beagle*'s commander. During the first expedition miserable weather, sickness and boredom accompanied the attempted survey of southern Chile, resulting in Captain Stokes' suicide. Now it was FitzRoy's turn for trouble. It began the moment the *Beagle* entered the Pacific Ocean.

First, it was the weather. FitzRoy expected an end to the storms that had pounded the *Beagle,* leaving all hands weak and confining Darwin to his hammock. As they turned north along the coast, the Pacific failed to live up to its name. Gale after sharp gale continued to batter the *Beagle* from the northwest. Then the ship's oldest officer, Rowlett, the purser, who had been ill for some time, died.

His solemn burial at sea plunged spirits still lower. FitzRoy finally took the *Beagle* into the lee of Chiloé Island and after three days pushed north again for Valparaiso, still 800 miles and several weeks sailing ahead of them.

During the slow weeks that followed, they left the rainy coasts behind. By the time the *Beagle* reached Valparaiso the weather was no longer a problem. "Everything appeared delightful," wrote Darwin. The weather was clear and dry, the temperature cool, but the winter sun brightened the whitewashed houses of the city. British men-of-war and merchant ships plied busily in and out of the harbor, which recently had become South America's most important on the west coast. Since Lord Cochrane had formed the fleet that helped liberate Peru at Valparaiso ten years before, the city had taken on a distinctly British character. Some said it was more reminiscent of an English seacoast village than a Chilean one.

Here, nonetheless, new problems confronted FitzRoy. For once, he wasn't sure what to do. The *Beagle* was to lay over in Valparaiso for several months while the charts and plans were drawn up from the past year's surveying. But the survey of Tierra del Fuego and the southernmost coast of Chile had not been completed to FitzRoy's satisfaction. Much to Darwin's horror, FitzRoy was considering returning to Tierra del Fuego, then surveying the entire coast, perhaps as far north as Guayaquil—a distance of 3,500 miles—before striking off westward across the Pacific. "That this voyage must come to a conclusion my reason tells me," wrote Darwin from Valparaiso, "but otherwise I see no end to it." FitzRoy's desire for a thorough survey was becoming an obsession.

Before any decision was to be made, the drafting of the charts had to be done. With customary fervor FitzRoy threw himself into analyzing soundings, astronomical sightings, and meteorological observations. He assigned Wickham as his substitute at the social gatherings which he would otherwise have been expected to attend.

Meanwhile, Darwin set off to enjoy some of the pleasures of civilization. By what he considered great fortune he discovered an old friend and Shrewsbury schoolmate, Richard Corfield, living in Valparaiso. Corfield immediately offered Darwin the use of his home as a base of operations for his adventures into the Andes.

Although it was mid-August—late winter for the Southern Hemisphere—and the high passes were still snowbound, Darwin left almost immediately on a brief excursion to the lower slopes. The ride took him through several haciendas, the Chilean counterpart of the Argentine *estancia,* and to Santiago, Chile's capital city. Riding horseback with guide and pack animals, he carried out the short trip in the same pattern as many of his other explorations. He planned to return to Corfield's by late September.

In Chile, Darwin observed many similarities to Argentina. The history and settlement of the two countries had a number of parallels. Before Spanish colonization both regions had been populated by Indians who had stopped the southernward expansion of the Incas and had then gone on to fight the Spanish. In Chile it was the Araucanians who still occupied the forested lands south of the Río Bío-Bío and would be the last warlike Indians to be subdued on the continent, some fifty years after the *Beagle*'s visit.

Similar to the lands near the Plata, Chile moreover was never an important part of Spain's South American empire. The Spanish conquistador Pedro Valdivia discovered the fertile central valley of Chile after crossing the brutally arid Atacama Desert from Peru. He had immediately recognized the agricultural potential of Chile, so reminiscent to him of the valleys of Andalusia in northern Spain. Santiago was founded in 1541. Yet agriculture was not Spain's aim. Suffering isolation at the farthest extremity of the Spanish Empire, Chile was colonized slowly, its early discoverers settling on their large landholdings granted by the crown, content to quietly raise large herds of cattle, plant orchards, and rule powerfully only on their own haciendas.

After Chile's war for independence there was little of the continual fighting and dislocation suffered by the countries to the north—Peru, Colombia, Bolivia, and Venezuela. Chile, like Argentina, suffered the battles of the *caudillos.* But by the early 1830's it had settled down with a constitution that was to last ninety years—something exceptional in South American history—and its first elected president. Of the former Spanish colonies eyed by England as a trading partner, Chile and Argentina were prime choices, a judgment proved sound during Darwin's lifetime.

In one momentous way Chile differed from Argentina; its geography. As Darwin noted, a glance at the map tells the beginning of the story. Chile is a string bean of a country, nowhere wider than 200 miles, a narrow strip of land wedged between the Pacific Ocean and the Andes. During Darwin's time its southern boundary, somewhere in Tierra del Fuego, was undefined. And it would take a brief war, fought years later, to draw a boundary in the north. Even then the country was well over 2,000 miles long.

This enormous extent, however, was Chile only as portrayed on the map. All the countries of South America during the 1830's —and today, for that matter—have large areas barely populated, if at all. The important part of a country is always smaller than the country defined by its boundaries.

For Chile, the important part of the country had been the middle since earliest colonization. In the north is the world's driest desert, the Atacama, where in places the parched earth has never been moistened by a drop of rain or shaded by the spiniest plant. In the south is the wet, cool forest that covers the land from the Andes west to the glacier-carved coast, the land of the Araucanian Indians and a few hardy settlers. Between these two extremes is the heart of Chile, dominated by a broad central valley much like the central valley of California. Here fertile soils and a temperate climate allow a rich harvest of grapes and citrus, wheat and corn.

On his excursion to the Andes, Darwin saw hacienda life and compared Chile's large estates to those he had visited in Brazil, Banda Oriental, and Argentina. Of the Chilean cowboy, he wrote:

The Guasos of Chile, who correspond to the Gauchos of the Pampas, are, however, a very different set of beings. Chile is the more civilized of the two countries, and the inhabitants, in consequence, have lost much individual character. Gradations in rank are much more strongly marked: the Guaso does not by any means consider every man his equal; and I was quite surprised to find that my companions did not like to eat at the same time with myself. This feeling of inequality is a necessary consequence of the existence of an aristocracy of wealth. It is said that some few of the greater landowners possess from five to ten thousand pounds sterling per annum: an inequality of riches which I believe is not met with, in any of the cattle-breeding countries eastward of the Andes. A traveller does not here meet that unbounded hospitality which refuses all payment, but yet is so kindly offered that no scruples can be raised in accepting it. Almost every house in Chile will receive you for the night, but a trifle is expected to be given in the morning; even a rich man will accept two or three shillings. The Gaucho, although he may be a cut-throat, is a gentleman; the Guaso is in few respects better, but at the same time a vulgar, ordinary fellow. The two men, although employed much in the same manner, are different in their habits and attire; and the peculiarities of each are universal in their respective countries. The Gaucho seems part of his horse, and scorns to exert himself excepting when on its back; the Gauso may be hired to work as a labourer in the fields. The former lives entirely on animal food; the latter almost wholly on vegetable. We do not here see the white boots, the broad drawers, and scarlet chilipa; the picturesque costume of the Pampas. Here, common trousers are protected by black and green worsted leggings. The poncho, however, is common to both. The chief pride of the Guaso lies in his spurs; which are absurdly large. I measured one which was six inches in the *diameter* of the rowel, and the rowel itself contained upwards of thirty points. . . . The Guaso is perhaps more expert with the lazo than the Gaucho; but, from the nature of the country, he does not know the use of the bolas.

The haciendas of Chile raised corn and wheat in addition to cattle, something which would have appalled most Argentine *estancieros.* Unlike the cattle ranches with their semi-nomadic gauchos, agriculture demanded workers tied to the land. Darwin found the agricultural workers of Chile, the *inquilinos,* much like the slaves of Brazil, living meager existences while the landowners enjoyed fine goods imported from Europe. The vast difference between rich and poor was the result of a system unquestioned then; it was one of life's unchangeable facts:

This poverty must be chiefly owing to the feudal-like system on which the land is tilled: the landowner gives a small plot of ground to the labourer, for building on and cultivating, and in return has his services . . . for every day of his life, without any wages. Until a father has a grown-up son, who can by his labour pay the rent, there is no one, except on occasional days, to take care of his own patch of ground. Hence extreme poverty is very common among the labouring classes in this country.

Of the countries visited by Darwin, the contrast between rich and poor was most apparent in Chile.

On his first jaunt Darwin would have liked to do more geologic work than he did. He spent one week at a copper mine at Jaguel, at the foot of the Andes, operated by a "shrewd but ignorant" miner from Cornwall who had married a Spanish girl. And he saw Santiago for the first time, describing it as smaller and not so fine as Buenos Aires, built on the same rectangular pattern as all of the former Spanish cities but with scenery "most striking" on the outskirts.

By September 24, 1834, he was on his way back to Valparaiso, feeling ill from what he thought at the time might have been bad country wine. But the last few miles he was so weak that he had to be carried. The illness was never diagnosed, but one belief is that Darwin had caught typhoid, a disease common in Chile. He spent the next six weeks in bed, "an inmate in Mr. Corfield's house."

Making matters worse was news from the *Beagle* about FitzRoy. While Darwin had been traveling in the Andes, FitzRoy had driven himself to exhaustion attempting to finish the charts, journal entries, and calculations of the survey. His temper was more volatile than ever, and the ship's physician was unable to give FitzRoy any prescription except rest.

The final blow to FitzRoy's already sinking spirit was struck by the Admiralty. At Valparaiso he received a harsh comminqué saying that the purchase of the *Adventure* would not be authorized. Furthermore, the added crews' expenses would not be carried on the *Beagle*'s pay sheet. In essence, their support during the last year had come from FitzRoy's own pocket. Trying to salvage something from the situation, FitzRoy managed to sell the *Adventure*. But the ordeal had been too much. In September, 1835, spiritually crushed and physically worn-out, Captain FitzRoy put himself on the sick list and resigned command of the *Beagle*.

Everyone was stunned by FitzRoy's resignation. For Darwin it was the low point of the trip. To be sure, he and FitzRoy had done their share of bickering over politics, slavery, and fossils, causing Darwin to comment: "We all stick to our former opinions rather more obstinately than before, and can give rather fewer reasons for doing so." Yet there was never any question about Fitz-Roy's skill at command. If Wickham took over, it meant the end of the *Beagle*'s voyage; under the ship's standing orders he would be bound to turn back for England.

Darwin could not imagine retracing his steps, and after enduring Tierra del Fuego, he was determined to see the west coast and the Andes. He went so far as to make plans to leave the *Beagle* and head north to Lima at his own expense, then travel over the Andes back to Buenos Aires, and from there to England. As for the expedition, FitzRoy's resignation meant that much of the west coast would remain unsurveyed and their measurements around the globe uncompleted.

Wickham, who would later become a captain in his own right, then governor of Queensland, Australia, joined with the rest of the ship's officers to change Fitz-Roy's mind. What would be gained by a resignation? Didn't the orders read to do as much of the survey as there was time for? Wouldn't it be better to complete the major tasks assigned to them and leave some of the details to be completed later? Finally, their obvious confidence in FitzRoy and their logic held sway. Wrote Darwin: "The Captain, at last, to everyone's joy, consented, and the resignation was withdrawn."

What is more, they would not return to Tierra del Fuego. They would go only as far south as the Chonos Archipelago before sailing north to Lima, then across the Pacific, island-hopping as they went. With FitzRoy back in command, Darwin wrote to his family: "For the first time since leaving England I now see a clear and not so distant prospect of returning to you all. . . . "

FitzRoy did intend to make one last trip south as far as the Chonos Archipelago. He originally planned to leave by late October. But he decided to wait until he could have Darwin aboard for the trip. Had Darwin known that the *Beagle* had been delayed because of his slow recovery, he would have felt all the worse. As it was, he noted that the six weeks spent flat on his back was "a grievous waste of time." On November 6, feeling almost well enough to join the crew's preparations for departure, he wrote a letter to his sister Catherine. He described the scare over FitzRoy's resignation, his chance meeting with Corfield, and his unfortunate illness. He also mentioned his ill luck "in only one little earthquake having happened." His voyage to the south of Chile would see his luck improve.

Although it wasn't apparent to most geologists then, the Andes are one of the most geologically active parts of the earth. The entire mountain chain suffers tremendous stress. Earthquakes result from a fracturing or rupture of strata due to these excessive strains. The cause of earthquakes, however, was still a hypothesis for future geologists. Such visible phenomena associated with earth-quakes as volcanic eruptions and so-called tidal waves had been observed since the time of the Greeks, though scientists explained them by the wildest theories. The common man or native living where earthquakes oc-curred had no more accurate an understanding of why they happened than did the scientists. But he did have an equally believable explanation: the will of the gods, punishment for some sin, or just plain bad luck. The entire west coast of South America had been frequently struck by severe earthquakes.

Most of November and all of December found the *Beagle* surveying the southern coast of Chile, one all too reminiscent of Tierra del Fuego. The coast was jagged and mountainous, its southern extremities receiving as much as 200 inches of rain per year. It was a rocky, dangerous coast, studded with islands, where shipwreck was common. "In winter the climate is detestable," wrote Darwin, "and in summer it is only a little better. . . . To have a week of fine weather is something wonderful."

By New Year's Day, 1835, the *Beagle* had completed most of the survey of the Chonos islands and was heading north through a heavy gale and steady rains, "ceremonies proper to it in these regions," to Chiloé, the largest, most northerly, and most populated of the coastal islands. By January 18 they were anchored at San Carlos Harbor on Chiloé's leeward side. The next evening the nearby volcano, Mount Orsorno, erupted, presenting a "magni-ficent spectacle." Darwin heard later that the volcano Aconcagua, just north of Santiago and Cosequina, far to the north, had also erupted.

On February 20, 1835, several hundred miles of Chilean coast were jolted by one of the most severe earthquakes in recorded history. The *Beagle* by then was at Valdivia, 150 miles north of Chiloé. When the earthquake struck, Darwin had been prowling the forests ashore and at the moment was stretched flat on his back, taking a rest:

It came on suddenly, and lasted two minutes, but the time appeared much longer. . . . There was no difficulty in standing upright, but the motion made me almost giddy: it was something like the movement of a vessel in a little cross-ripple, or still more like that felt by a person skating over thin ice, which bends under the weight of his body.

A bad earthquake at once destroys our oldest associations: the earth, the very emblem of solidity, has moved beneath our feet like a thin crust over a fluid—one second of time has created in the mind a strange idea of insecurity. . . . In the forest, as a breeze moved the trees, I felt only the earth tremble, but saw no other effect. Captain FitzRoy and some officers were at the town during the shock, and there the scene was more striking; for although the houses, from being built of wood, did not fall, they were violently shaken, and the boards creaked and rattled together. The people rushed out of doors in the greatest alarm. It is these accompaniments that create that perfect horror of earthquakes. . . .

At Valdivia, though most of the houses were left standing, it had been the worst earthquake remembered by the oldest inhabitant. Two hundred miles farther north, at Concepción, not a building was upright. When the *Beagle* entered the harbor at Concepción, they found the coast littered with timber and strewn with furniture "as if a thousand ships had been wrecked." To Darwin it was an awful yet interesting spectacle, his sympathy with the inhabitants and his scientific curiosity working with equal intensity. The *Beagle* spent three days at Concepción, and after viewing the havoc, Darwin wrote:

... I cannot understand how the greater number of inhabitants escaped unhurt. The houses in many parts fell outwards; thus forming in the middle of the streets little hillocks of brickwork and rubbish. Mr. Rouse, the English consul, told us that he was at breakfast when the first movement warned him to run out. He had scarcely reached the middle of the courtyard, when one side of his house came thundering down. . . . As shock succeeded shock, at the interval of a few minutes, no one dared approach the shattered ruins; and no one knew whether his dearest friends and relations were not perishing from the want of help. Those who had saved any property were obliged to keep a constant watch, for thieves prowled about, and at each little trembling of the gound, with one hand they beat their breasts and cried "misericordia!" and then with the other filched what they could from the ruins. The thatched roofs fell over the fires, and flames burst forth in all parts. Hundreds knew themselves ruined, and few had the means of providing food for the day.

Earthquakes alone are sufficient to destroy the prosperity of any country. . . .

But the scientific side of Darwin's mind looked at the earthquake as a way in which vast tracts of land could be modified, and he wrote:

The most remarkable effect of this earthquake was the permanent elevation of the land; it would probably be far more correct to speak of it as the cause. There can be no doubt that the land round the Bay of Concepcion was upraised two or three feet. . . .

As the *Beagle* sailed from Concepción back to Valparaiso, Darwin was planning one more journey into the Andes to wind up his work on South American geology.

The *Beagle* arrived at Valparaiso on March 11, and two days later Darwin was off across the Andes to Mendoza with a friend, a mule driver, and eleven mules stocked with extra food, lest an early snow leave them stranded on one of the high passes over the mountains. FitzRoy, meanwhile, turned the *Beagle* around and, in his ever-thorough fashion, returned to Concepción to complete a detailed study of the effects of the earthquake. They would meet later at Valparaiso before sailing north to survey the arid coast of the Atacama.

Measured in a straight line, Mendoza was scarcely 100 miles from Santiago. Between the two cities lay the Andes, which Darwin likened to a great wall, guarding Chile's frontier better than the sea. With crests more than 20,000 feet high and white-capped peaks occasionally extending even higher, the Andes were a more overwhelming spectacle than he had anticipated. They were a proper climax for Darwin's study of South America's geology.

By then Darwin had finished volumes two and three of Lyell's *Principles of Geology*, and he admitted, at least to his cousin Fox, that he was a "zealous disciple." By then, too, his hammer had pounded away at granite in Brazil, dug fossils from sediments of the Pampas and helped his speculations about the stony covering of Patagonia's plains. It is impossible to tell when all this added up to change many of Darwin's speculations to convictions. By his final trip into the Andes, it is certain that the ideas of Lyell were guides to his own studies.

Darwin's idea was that the Andes had been slowly upheaved over a long period of time and that the rivers and streams that flowed from the snow-crested peaks wore away at the mountains and helped build the plateau of Patogonia with their deposits. They had also filled the great central valley of Chile with sediments that created the fertile soil. The common belief then was that the Andes were the product of one huge volcanic catastrophe.

During the first brief trip into the Andes, Darwin discovered fossil seashells far above the present level of the sea which once must have lived in the shallow ocean margins. The earthquake at Concepción demonstrated to him the manner in which land could be raised a few feet at a time. During the second excursion he found additional fossil shells and layers of sedimentary rock which, like the shells, had once been deposited when rivers had flowed into a body of water and later were elevated to their present altitude by an endless number of small upheavals. Some of these seashells were found 12,000 feet above the sea.

One of the main objectives of the second trip was to accumulate samples which would support his hypothesis.

Darwin felt that without an overwhelming abundance of proof, he would never be able to convince such conservative and cautious geologists as Sedgwick and Henslow. This patient collection of evidence to support his ideas was a characteristic of Darwin's later scientific work.

Darwin's studies of South American geology overwhelmingly vindicated the principles of Lyell. There was no reason to suppose that the processes he observed could not have accounted for the shape of the earth's crust without the idea of catastrophe. Moreover Darwin by then had begun to grasp the enormity of geologic time, which would later be a major argument in explaining how evolution could occur.

After a night high on the Andes, camped by one of the streams that flowed miles distant into the sea, Darwin wrote one passage that offered a glimpse of his realizations:

Amidst the din of rushing waters, the noise from the stones, as they rattled one over another, was most distinctly audible even from a distance. This rattling noise, night and day, may be heard along the whole course of the torrent. The sound spoke eloquently to the geologist; the thousands and thousands of stones, which, striking against each other . . . were all hurrying in one direction. It was like thinking on time, where the minute that now glides past is irrecoverable. So was it that these stones; the ocean is their eternity, and each note of that wild music told of one more step towards their destiny.

It is not possible for the mind to comprehend, except by a slow process, any effect which is produced by a cause repeated so often. . . . As often as I have seen beds of mud, sand, and shingle, accumulated to the thickness of many thousand feet, I have felt inclined to exclaim that causes, such as the present rivers and the present beaches, could never have ground down and produced such masses. But, on the other hand, when listening to the rattling noise of these torrents, and calling to mind that whole races of animals have passed away from the face of the earth, and that during this whole period, night and day, these stones have gone rattling onwards in their course, I have thought to myself, can any mountains, any continent, withstand such waste?

The entire second journey into the Andes lasted for twenty-four days, and to Darwin's thinking it had been one of the best. They had reached Mendoza via Portillo Pass, south of Santiago, and though higher and more dangerous than Uspallata Pass, farther north, they missed with good luck an early snow.

Mendoza turned out to be a "stupid" little town, economically decaying since the days it had prospered at the entrance to Uspallata Pass, guarding Spain's trade that went over the Andes. Darwin was further inconvenienced during the one night he spent there by the persistent bites, which he more likened to attacks, of a black bug called the *benchuca*. Like the mosquito, the *benchuca* was a bloodsucker, and later medical research found it also to be a carrier of disease. Darwin returned to Valparaiso via Uspallata Pass and Santiago and reached there in high spirits, one of his mules loaded with rock samples and specimens.

When Darwin had first arrived in Valparaiso nine months before, he had written despondently to Whitley: "What will become of me hereafter I know not; I feel like a ruined man, who does not see or care to extricate himself." On April 23, 1835, a week following his Andean adventure, he wrote Susan enthusiastically about the trip, adding: "I literally could hardly sleep at nights for thinking over my day's work." His growing confidence in his own ability to theorize was readily apparent. "Since leaving England," he wrote, "I have never made so successful a journey. . . . "

11

Where Rain Never Falls
APRIL, 1835–OCTOBER, 1836

POTOSÍ was the largest and richest city built by the Spanish in the Western Hemisphere. From the mid-1500's, when a great mountain of silver was discovered 13,000 feet in the Andes, until the rich veins were depleted 150 years later, Potosí was the economic heart of South America, its riches pouring from the highlands to Lima. By the mid-1600's, when the English population of North America was but a few thousand, Potosí held 160,000 people, 95,000 of these Indians forced to labor in the mines. During the first 50 years of production, 60,000,000 pounds of silver were taken from Potosí, worth $400,000,000 at today's value.

During the colonial years Chile never produced wealth comparable to that of Upper Peru, which in 1826 became Bolivia. With the potential riches the Andes had to yield, the early settlers scoured the valleys and foothills, but fortunes came to few. In his geologic work, Darwin came across the pocks and scars that evidenced the mining fever possessing many a Chilean, and he wrote that "the rage for mining has left scarcely a spot in Chile unexamined."

Several rich silver deposits —but nothing of the magnitude of Potosí —had been recently discovered in Chile, and the semiarid region north of Santiago had become dotted with small mining communities. Yet it was two other minerals, copper and sodium nitrate, neither of importance during the 1830's, that would make Chile wealthy. Copper mining then was a small industry thought to be a conservative occupation compared with the chance of real wealth —exploring and mining silver.

Large deposits of sodium nitrate had been known for some time, but a use for the chalky gray rock was a recent discovery. In 1809 a German scientist suggested the value of sodium nitrate as a fertilizer. Commonly called saltpeter, sodium nitrate was also a major component for gunpowder. Neither fertilizer nor gunpowder was of much use to Chile. Before the end of the nineteenth century, however, Chilean nitrates would enrich the soils of the American cotton belt, the fields and farms of Europe, and the depleted soils of Egypt's Nile Delta. Chile's first shipment of nitrate was sent only four years before Darwin's visit —110 tons bound for England.

Mining succeeded in populating parts of Chile which an economy based on agriculture or cattle could never have reached. North of the central valley of Chile the climate becomes more arid with each mile, until beyond the valley of Copiapó, 400 miles north of Santiago, scarcely a drop of rain has ever fallen. This is the beginning of the Atacama Desert, and it stretches north from Copiapó for more than 600 miles, its arid extent broken only once by an oasis, where the Loa River fights its way from the Andes to the sea. But in the arid wastes and in the only slightly less arid land between Santiago and Copiapó, gold, silver, and copper were discovered. Darwin ventured northward from Valparaiso to the mining town of Copiapó in the midst of a silver boom after little more than catching his breath from his trip to the Andes. He left by horseback April 27.

Three weeks' ride ahead was the small village of Coquimbo, halfway to Copiapó. Receiving but four and a half inches of rain a year, Coquimbo had little to commend it except that it had one of the finest harbors on the entire west coast, with white sandy beaches ideal for careening. While Darwin made his way toward Coquimbo by horseback, FitzRoy sailed there with the *Beagle* for final overhauling before the long journey across the Pacific.

Leaving Valparaiso, Darwin and his guides followed the coast before turning inland to visit the mining districts. The mines were crudely and quickly built with the most simple machinery, human labor being far cheaper and more easily replaceable than machines. In places the hillsides had been so tunneled they looked to Darwin like ant nests. The miner's life appeared little better than that of one of his packhorses, and he was surprised that miserable as it was, the miners considered their lot a better one than that of the *inquilino* who plodded through life tied to his *patrón* and an acre or two of land.

The Chilian miners are a peculiar race of men in their habits. Living for weeks together in the most desolate spots, when they descend to the villages on feast-days, there is no excess or extravagance into which they do not run. They sometimes gain a considerable sum, and then, like sailors with prize-money, they try how soon they can contrive to squander it. They drink excessively, buy quantities of clothes, and in a few days return penniless to their miserable abodes, there to work harder than beasts of burden. This thoughtlessness, as with sailors, is evidently the result of a similar manner of life. Their daily food is found them, and they acquire no habits of carefulness; moreover, temptation and the means of yielding to it are placed in their power at the same time. . . .

At one mine Darwin saw the workers bring heavy ore baskets up rickety ladders from a depth of 600 feet, forbidden to halt for a breath. Darwin weighed one load at 197 pounds and was assured that it was below average. Each miner brought twelve loads a day to the surface and in between picked and broke the rock below in the shaft. Yet the men, fed mainly on beans and cracked wheat, appeared to Darwin to be healthy and cheerful, "a wonderful instance of the amount of labour which habit, for it can be nothing else, will enable a man to endure."

Dining with a mine manager one night, Darwin was told about the large number of foreigners, especially Englishmen, who had now spread over the country. But it had not always been so. When the mine manager was a boy, he told Darwin, nothing would have induced him to go near an Englishman, "so deeply had they been impressed with an idea of the heresy, contamination, and evil to be derived from contact with such a person. To this day they relate the atrocious actions of the bucaniers. . . ."

Not everyone Darwin encountered on the ride to Coquimbo had lost his suspicions of the English. Riding through the coastal villages which the *Beagle* had passed a few days before, Darwin was amused to hear that they believed the ship a smuggler, and all the more successful because her captain refused to bargain. Darwin wrote in his diary, "A person who could possibly mistake Capt. FitzRoy for a smuggler, would never perceive any difference between a Lord Chesterfield and his valet." Darwin reached Coquimbo on May 14. A week later he continued north to Copiapó. The *Beagle* meanwhile returned to Valparaiso for a final provisioning for the long journey across the Pacific. FitzRoy planned to pick up Darwin at Copiapó before the last leg of the journey in South America, to Lima.

The valley of Copiapó is the last ribbon of green before the Atacama. Darwin compared the valley to an island surrounded not by sea but by sand. He arrived June 22, his horse having been without food or water for more than two days.

I am tired of repeating the epithets barren and sterile. These words, however, as commonly used, are comparative; I have always applied them to the plains of Patagonia, which can boast of spiny bushes and some tufts of grass; and this is absolute fertility, as compared with northern Chile. . . .

It was the end of his last major expedition in South America.

On May 2 the *Beagle* arrived, under Wickham's command. At Valparaiso, FitzRoy had heard that the H.M.S. *Challenger* had been wrecked along the southern coast and, taking one of the *Beagle*'s whaleboats, had joined with another British ship, the H.M.S. *Blond,* to rescue the *Challenger*'s crew. He would catch up with them at Callao, seaport for Lima, the former capital of Spain's South American empire.

For 200 years Lima had been the capital and center of Spanish South America and the most modern, cultured, and glorious city on the continent, second only to Potosí in size. The conquistador Francisco Pizarro founded Lima in 1535, the year following his defeat of the Incas.

Like the other cities to follow, Lima was built according to royal plan. A rectangular street pattern was laid out, with a plaza at its center. On one side of the plaza a cathedral was built; on the other side a town hall, the seat of government. As an administrative center controlling trade and affairs from Panama to Buenos Aires, the number of government buildings quickly multiplied.

The plaza, as in every Spanish city from California to Chiloé Island, was the stage where the drama of public life was displayed. Royal visitors were received in the plaza, festivals were held there, and later it was the site where the Inquisition condemned the unfaithful. It was a place for weekly markets and gory bullfights. The steps of the town hall were most likely the spot where independence was declared and where after independence *caudillos* made their speeches. But in the days before the *caudillos,* the plaza at Lima witnessed the greatest spectacles imaginable, all of it due to the wealth of silver that came from the mines of Potosi.

At Potosí the silver was smeltered and, less the fifth for the crown, ended up in the pockets of the many government and church administrators in Lima. In 1683 Lima was such a wealthy city that the businessmen welcomed a new governor general by lining two streets with bricks of silver. Several times each year a fleet of ships would leave Callao heavy with silver, cacao, skins, and Vicuña wool and sail north to Panama City. From Panama the heavy burdens were carried across the narrow neck of land by mule to Portobello. There the silver was eagerly awaited by merchants loaded with trade goods from Spain. For a few weeks, Portobello was the trading center of the empire. Stacks of silver wedges on the wharf were traded swiftly for silk, porcelain, fine linens, and perfumes. Then the fleet would return to Lima to distribute, as best it could, goods to the other parts of South America. The best, of course, stayed with the myriad government and church officials of the capital. For two centuries Lima lived up to its name —the City of Kings.

During the 1700's the empire changed, and so did Lima. The impossibility of administering all parts of a growing empire and forcing trade only through Lima became more apparent. The great fleets to Panama were abolished in 1723, and other ports opened to trade with Spain. By 1776 La Plata was prosperous enough to become a vice royalty equal with Peru, wealth from its vast territories pouring through the customhouses of Buenos Aires, forever by-passing Lima. By 1700, moreover, the ores of Potosí had been nearly depleted. Revolt by enslaved Indian miners, earthquakes —as frequent in Peru as in Chile —and economic decline combined to dull the glitter of the City of Kings. By the end of the 1700's Lima was past its prime, a minor trading and administrative center for an empire on the verge of disintegration. It was then that Alexander von Humboldt visited the city.

Lima and its seaport, Callao, were the only cities visited in common by Darwin and his university idol, Alexander von Humboldt. Humboldt spent two months there in 1802 and found Lima a small, dilapidated town without well-furnished homes or beautiful women. Darwin's impressions of Lima were much the same:

The city of Lima is now in a wretched state of decay: the streets are nearly unpaved; and heaps of filth are piled up in all directions, where the black gallinazos, tame as poultry, pick up bits of carrion. . . . The City of Kings, must formerly have been a splendid town. . . .

The *Beagle* anchored at Callao on July 19. It was midwinter, and though the temperatures at that latitude were never low, the sky was overcast and gray. For more than half a year the coast of the Atacama and as far north as Lima is covered by low clouds; they are caused by the prevailing winds from the west sweeping across a cold ocean current that moves northward along the coast, its origins far south in icy Arctic waters. Humboldt first measured the temperature of the current. During Darwin's time it was known as the Humboldt Current, a name used until oceanographers renamed it the Peru Current in this century.

The current influences the weather of nearly 1,000 miles of South American coast. The air that passes over the cold current is chilled, then warms as it strikes land. Meteorologically such a circumstance never produces rain, yet is responsible, nonetheless, for the cloudy sameness of the coastal climate. Only in summer—the months from December through April—do the sun's rays become strong enough to disperse the clouds, bathing the coast in day after day of brilliant sunlight. Darwin saw none of this. Of the first sixteen days at Lima, the air was clear enough only once for him to see the Andes, which lie as a backdrop to the city.

Waiting for FitzRoy, the *Beagle* anchored at Callao for six weeks. Darwin found the city small, filthy, and ill built. The poor weather and Callao's filth didn't bother him as much as the political unrest that kept him from venturing much beyond the limits of the city. Far worse than those of the countries near the Plata, the civil war in Peru had been long and bitter. As the center of the Spanish Empire, sympathy with the crown was high, and the majority of people had no desire for independence. Peru was among the last regions to win independence, and the bitter fight among *caudillos* was still continuing when Darwin visited.

At the time of our visit, there were four chiefs in arms contending for supremacy in the government: if one succeeded in becoming for a time very powerful, the others coalesced against him; but no sooner were they victorious, than they were again hostile to each other. The other day, at the Anniversary of the Independence, high mass was performed, the President partaking of the sacrament . . . instead of each regiment displaying the Peruvian flag, a black one with death's head unfurled. Imagine a government under which such a scene could be ordered, on such an occasion, to be typical of their determination of fighting to death!

By the time FitzRoy arrived at Callao, reporting that the crew of the *Challenger* had been rescued, Darwin had only explored a few Indian ruins, the wrecked city of old Callao destroyed by the earthquake of 1746, and examined the terraces and small islands along the coast. "I cannot say I liked the very little I saw of Peru," he remarked.

With FitzRoy back in command, the *Beagle* left the west coast of South America behind. Their first port of call was an unimportant group of volcanic islands called the Galápagos. Their singular geology caused Darwin to write Fox from Lima, mentioning that "I look forward to the Galápagos with more interest than any other part of the voyage." They were to live up to his expectations, to exceed them in fact, but in ways that Darwin never then suspected and wouldn't realize until the *Beagle*'s voyage had ended.

Other than being annexed by Ecuador in 1831, the Galápagos were not part of South America at all. Situated 600 miles west of the continent, its twelve large islands and hundreds of smaller ones are geologically distinct, built from the deep ocean floor by layer upon layer of volcanic lava. They are in the truest sense islands of the deep sea. Among the sights that led Darwin to his thoughts on evolution, his discoveries on the Galápagos were the most important.

The islands themselves belied their importance. Their history had been insignificant. In the years between the Spanish discovery in 1535 and the annexation by Ecuador, to which they still belong, their main value was to buccaneers, who had used the Galápagos as a base from which to raid Spanish ships and sack the villages along the west coast. In the mid 1600's the British pirate William Dampier gave the islands many English names which they still carried at the time the *Beagle* arrived. The remainder were supplied by a British survey ship in 1794.

This early British survey was in anticipation of the Pacific's becoming a whaling ground. Islands were needed where whalers could take on water, exchange information, and if possible use what provisions the island could offer. As barren, craggy, and dry as the Galápagos were, their name is a clue to the unique provisions the islands offered whaler and pirate alike. Galápagos is the name the Spanish gave the huge, slow-moving land tortoises that ambled over the islands in thousands. Fresh turtle meat was no small prize. When the *Beagle* sighted the islands on September 15, 1835, a small colony of several hundred people, with an Englishman as vice-governor, was keeping itself alive by farming and tortoise hunting.

Strewn across the equator under the strong rays of the tropical sun, the Galápagos, but for one reason, would have looked like the typical islands of the tropics, their mountain peaks bathed by white clouds, the slopes covered by green, and the beaches lined with the coconut palm. But the Galápagos fell under the influence of the Peru Current, where the cold waters bent away from the coast on their gigantic counterclockwise movement that would eventually bring them back once again to the Antarctic. Instead of tropical islands, the Galápagos were fog-shrouded and arid. The lava that built them was deprived of sun and rain and barely eroded. Their vegetation appeared more Arctic than tropical. Yet during the month and five days the *Beagle* remained among the islands, Darwin discovered the Galápagos to be biologically "a little world within itself."

Overwhelmingly, the plants and animals Darwin discovered were new species found nowhere else on earth. Of more than fifty species of land birds Darwin collected, twenty-six were separate species of finch, "all . . . peculiar to this archiepelago." The reptiles gave the islands a striking character and, of those, the giant tortoises were the most amazing. Ashore on Chatham Island, Darwin describes his first encounter with these tortoises:

The day was glowing hot, and the scrambling over the rough surface and through the intricate thickets, was very fatiguing; but I was well repaid by the strange Cyclopean scene. As I was walking along I met two large tortoises, each of which must have weighed at least two hundred pounds: one was eating a piece of cactus, and as I approached, it stared at me and slowly stalked away; the other gave a deep hiss, and drew in its head. These huge reptiles, surrounded by the black lava, the leafless shrubs, and large cacti, seemed to my fancy like some antediluvian animals. The few dull-coloured birds cared no more for me, than they did for the great tortoises.

The tortoises fascinated Darwin, and he studied and described them with his customary preciseness. He found that on some islands they preferred to live in the high, damp regions, on other islands in the low, arid parts. He found what they ate. He measured the rate of which they gulped "great mouthfuls" of water —"about ten in a minute" —and the speed they traveled —"four miles a day." Like the proverbial tortoise that raced with the hare, "the tortoises, when purposely moving towards any point, travel by night and day, and arrive at their journey's end much sooner than would be expected." He studied their breeding habits, found out they were deaf, even rode their backs for no better reason than wild curiosity, though he found them a difficult mount to stay on. Yet he nearly missed the most important fact of all.

A few days before the *Beagle* was to leave, Darwin was discussing the tortoises with the vice-governor, Mr. Lawson. Lawson told him that the tortoises on each island were slightly different and that he could tell which island one was from if it were shown to him.

I did not for some time pay sufficient attention to this statement, and I had already partially mingled together the collections from two of the islands. I never dreamed that islands, about fifty or sixty miles apart, and most of them in sight of each other, formed of precisely the same rocks, placed under a quite similar climate, rising to a nearly equal height, would have been differently tenanted. . . .

The tortoises were not only found in no other part of the world but the Galápagos, but each of the major islands had separate species. In addition to the finches, Darwin found the same uniqueness among plants, many native to only one of the Galápagos Islands, found nowhere else on earth.

This, then, was the key to the question that Darwin must certainly have begun to ask himself. Why had the "Creative force" been so lavished on the Galápagos? Why should there be so many separate species of finch that differed only slightly, mainly in the shape of their beak? Why should there be two species of lizard so similar in form, except that one was near the edge of the sea, feeding on seaweeds under the water, venturing ashore only when frightened, the other only an inhabitant of the land? A divine planner had spent an inordinate amount of attention on the creation of species for the Galápagos, unless of course there was some other explanation.

From the Galápagos the *Beagle* continued across the Pacific, sailing southwest, stopping briefly at Tahiti and putting the unfortunate missionary Reverend Matthews ashore in New Zealand to stay with his brother. By then Darwin was restless for home. From Sydney, Australia, in January 1836, Darwin wrote Henslow that he was "never intended for a traveller; my thoughts are always rambling over past or future scenes; I cannot enjoy the present happiness for anticipating the future, which is about as foolish as the dog who dropped the real bone for its shadow."

To make it worse, after rounding the tip of Africa, instead of proceeding directly to England, FitzRoy decided to complete his circle of measurements all in the Southern Hemisphere. He set a course for their first port of call more than four years before, Salvador, on the coast of Brazil. It was from there Darwin wrote Susan that FitzRoy's "zigzag manner" had put the finishing stroke to the feelings. "I loath, I abhor the sea and all ships which sail on it."

By then even the tropical forest failed to lift Darwin's sinking enthusiasm. He was ready for the *Beagle*'s long voyage to end.

On October 2, 1836, the *Beagle* landed at the small harbor of Falmouth in southern England, and by the morning of the fifth Darwin had walked into his home at Shrewsbury, catching the family at breakfast. Two days later Darwin wrote Henslow that he was "giddy with joy and confusion."

12

The Great Mystery

WHEN ON board the H.M.S. *"Beagle,"* as natur-
alist, I was much struck with certain facts in the distribution of
the organic beings inhabiting South America, and in the
geological relations of the present to the past inhabitants of
that continent. These facts . . . seemed to throw some light on
the origin of species —that mystery of mysteries, as it has been
called by one of our greatest philosophers.

Thus began the first paragraph of Darwin's epoch-
making book, the *Origin of Species.* Despite the inspiration provided by what he saw in South America, it would
be twenty-two years following the *Beagle*'s return before
he would write these words. The time Darwin spent on his
theory of evolution spanned much of his life.

During the last months of the *Beagle*'s voyage, FitzRoy read part of Darwin's diary and thought it worth publishing. On returning to England, FitzRoy made arrangements for Darwin's journal to make up the third volume of the official history of the *Beagle*'s two voyages, FitzRoy and Captain King authoring the first two. Darwin began sorting out his collections and rewriting his notes almost immediately, the idea of the ministry apparently vanishing even from the thoughts of his father. The first draft of his journal was finished in June, 1837.

As Darwin sifted through his notes and the materials from the voyage in the tranquillity of rooms at Cambridge, the pieces of the puzzle came together. The following month he secretly started a notebook to collect information and facts for a species theory. In his pocket diary he wrote: "In July opened first note-book on Transmutation of Species. Had been greatly struck from about the month of Previous March [1836] on character of South American fossils, and species of Galápagos Archipelago. These facts (especially latter), origin of all my views."

Much in the manner that Lyell had gathered evidence for *Principles of Geology,* Darwin began collecting a vast variety of information, not quite knowing where it would lead. As he noted, "no one has a right to speculate without distinct facts." For the next twenty years, notwithstanding his other projects, the collection of facts to shed light on evolution was a major concern.

In the year 1837 his *Journal of Researches* was printed, though not published until 1839, pending the completion of FitzRoy's volume. The journal would be published separately in 1845, known in the United States as the

Darwin's study at Down, where he lived after 1842.
COURTESY AMERICAN MUSEUM OF NATURAL HISTORY.

Voyage of the Beagle. As his first literary child, he nurtured a special affection for the book. The 1845 edition of *Voyage of the Beagle* was dedicated to Charles Lyell, whom he met the year following the *Beagle*'s return.

In the years following the voyage, Darwin's life changed considerably. He became single-minded about science, losing his fondness for poetry, music, and Shakespeare. The year following the beginning of the notebook on species, he married Uncle Josiah's daughter Emma, his cousin, and three years later they moved out of hectic London to the village of Down, 30 miles away. At Down, Darwin spent the rest of his life, occasionally entertaining the Lyells and the Henslows and working in the large study among piles of scientific books, journals and table-top experiments. After the *Beagle,* he traveled little.

One of the reasons was recurring poor health, the cause of which has never been diagnosed. One feeling is that in his later years Darwin became a bit of a hypochondriac, compounded by physical exhaustion linked to his complete mental absorption in what he was doing. The harder he worked, the worse he felt. Another belief is that Darwin caught Chagas disease from the bite of the *benchuca* in Mendoza, a disease diagnosed only in 1934. The symptoms were the same: lack of energy, shivering, nausea, all amounting to a semi-invalidism.

Whatever the cause, sickness plagued him for the remainder of his life, robbing him of precious energy. He worked a maximum of four hours a day, often losing weeks to unshakable bouts of illness. He accustomed himself to take advantage of every small amount of time to work. The main idea underlying his working method was to make the minutes count.

In October, 1838, the same year he married Emma, Darwin chanced to read "for amusement" the gloomy little *Essay on the Principles of Population,* written by Thomas Malthus. One of Malthus' ideas struck a note with Darwin. According to Malthus, the food resources of the world were bound to increase in a simple mathematical ratio . . . one, two, three, four. But man, with each individual able to have many offspring, would increase in numbers geometrically . . . two, four, eight, sixty-four. With population rapidly exceeding food supply, Malthus predicted a tremendous struggle for food and space, the mortality of the losers a way by which the population would be kept in check. Reflected Darwin:

. . . being well prepared to appreciate the struggle for existence which everywhere goes on from long-continued observation of the habits of animals and plants, it at once struck me that under these circumstances favourable variations would tend to be preserved, and unfavourable ones to be destroyed. The result of this would be the formation of new species. Here then I had at last got a theory by which to work; but I was so anxious to avoid prejudice, that I determined not for some time to write even the briefest sketch of it.

By 1842 Darwin was convinced about the fact of evolution and had hit on the concept of natural selection as a mechanism by which evolution could occur. He allowed himself the "satisfaction" of outlining it in a brief abstract of 35 pages. He expanded this in 1844 into an essay of 230 pages containing much of what later would become the *Origin of Species*. He confided the existence of the sketch to his wife, Emma, and on January 11, 1844, wrote the young botanist John Hooker —who with Lyell became one of his closest friends —telling him of his idea.

... I have been now ever since my return engaged in a very presumptuous work, and I know no one individual who would not say a very foolish one. I was so struck with the distribution of the Galápagos organisms, &c. &c., and with the character of the American fossil mammifers, &c. &c., that I determined to collect blindly every sort of fact, which could bear any way on what are species. I have read heaps of agricultural and horticultural books, and have never ceased collecting facts. At last gleams of light have come, and I am almost convinced (quite contrary to the opinion I started with) that species are not (it is like confessing a murder) immutable.

Still, Darwin felt he needed more evidence. While he worked on a geology of South America, an exhausting eight-year study of barnacles, and various minor projects, the subject of species was never far from his mind. By 1855 it became his full-time occupation. He bred pigeons, cultivated and crossbred plants, counted orchid seeds, compared animal skeletons, and kept thick folders on different breeds of horses and ducks. To account for the dispersal of some species over wide areas, he experimented by immersing seeds in ocean water to see if they could have been transported by ocean currents while still maintaining the ability to germinate. He dissected plants and animals and examined botanical collections. He groaned through mounds of technical books and papers in English, French and —particularly painful for him— German. Darwin's main drive was to anticipate the arguments he would receive beforehand and to offer evidence against them. It was a mammoth task for even so patient a man as Darwin.

Through it all, a steady correspondence with Lyell and Hooker provided him with a sounding board for his ideas. Though skeptical about many of Darwin's conclusions— for example, his continuing disbelief that plants and animals could have migrated across land bridges that have since sunk beneath the sea, a theory since disproven —Lyell encouraged Darwin's work. Darwin appreciated Lyell's patience and later wrote: "When I made any remark to him on Geology, he never rested until he saw the whole case clearly. . . . He would advance all possible objections to my suggestion, and even after these were exhausted would long remain dubious."

Sir Joseph Dalton Hooker had recently returned from India and was becoming one of the most influential botanists in England. Furthermore, he was an active member of the British Association and the Linnean Society, whose scientific meetings Darwin seldom attended. In 1854 Darwin scribbled a note that Hooker would be the best man to edit his 1844 sketch, should anything ever happen to him. With their patient querying, anticipation of arguments, and gentle encouragement, Hooker and Lyell helped Darwin toward the day when he would finally stop collecting and begin writing.

Both Lyell and Hooker showed a measure of friendly impatience that Darwin should wait so long to make his ideas known. Even his brother Erasmus warned that someone was likely to beat him to it. But for Darwin the value of a detailed work was more important than the pleasure of being first.

In 1856 Darwin gave in to Lyell's continued urging and began writing a book, tentatively called *Natural Selection.* It would be a long book, he warned, as detailed and perfect as he could make it. Nineteen years had passed since he had opened his first notebook on evolution, and Darwin probably would never have published the *Origin of Species* scarcely three years later if it had not been for another naturalist quietly working 3,000 miles from England in the jungles of the Malay Archipelago.

On June 18, 1859, two years after Darwin began writing the "big book," he found among the letters in the daily mail a brief note from a young naturalist he had corresponded with several times named Alfred Russell Wallace. Wallace was a competent field naturalist and had spent many years in the jungles of the Amazon and Malaya. Just the year before, Lyell had recommended to Darwin an admirable scientific paper Wallace had written.

Attached to the letter Darwin received that day was a brief scientific paper outlining an idea that had come to Wallace when he was sick with fever on Ternate Island in the Moluccas. Wallace asked Darwin if he would please read his sketch and, if he thought it worthwhile, to forward it to Lyell. Darwin read Wallace's paper with a sinking feeling. There, in crisp, succinct prose was a theory of evolution with natural selection as the principle mechanism. Reading Wallace's words was like reading his own. "Even his terms now," Darwin wrote Lyell, "stand as heads of my chapters." Working separately, Wallace had come to the exact same conclusion as Darwin. Suddenly Darwin found himself not quite so unconcerned about being first to publish the theory. Though Darwin had hit upon the idea of natural selection long before Wallace, publishing his idea with Wallace's sketch there in front of him troubled his conscience. Turning to Lyell, he wrote, ". . . as I had not intended to publish any sketch, can I do so honourably, because Wallace has sent me an outline of his doctrine? I would far rather burn my whole book, than that he or any other man should think that I had behaved in a paltry spirit." Again Lyell and Hooker came up with good advice and a plan.

Three months later Wallace's paper, along with excerpts from Darwin's essay of 1844 and a letter he had previously written outlining his idea to the American geologist Asa Gray, were published jointly in the journal of the Linnean Society. When the joint paper was read at the society's meeting, it was received with some surprise, but on the whole rather quietly.

Feeling the world would not wait much longer, Lyell and Hooker urged Darwin to begin working on a version of his book for publication. What Darwin first began as an abstract for the Linnean Society's journal ended up thirteen months later as a book. In the fashion of the time its title was thoroughly descriptive: *An Abstract of an Essay on the Origin of Species and Varieties Through Natural Selection.* Despite being called "an abstract of an essay," it was a long book. Much to the benefit of later readers, it was perhaps only one-fourth the length of

Darwin's originally intended treatment and less detailed. The first printing of 1,250 copies was large for that time; even Darwin felt it was an ambitious estimate. The *Origin of Species* was published November 24, 1859, selling out to booksellers the first day.

The book had two major themes. First, the *Origin of Species* was an overwhelming argument documenting the fact of evolution. According to Darwin the plants and animals of the earth today are the descendants of former species now extinct. In fact, all life on earth might be found to be related by tracing present and extinct species back along treelike branches of evolution to common ancestors. Although Darwin was careful to avoid man in most of his discussion, he did indicate in the conclusion that what applied to the world of plants and animals must also be considered applicable to man.

The second major theme was a discussion of natural selection as a means whereby evolution might occur. Without the hypothesis explaining how, the idea of evolution was not enough. Without Darwin's theory of natural selection, the *Origin of Species* would perhaps have been an imposing but short-lived work. Natural selection, he felt, was his great discovery.

The idea behind natural selection is that a struggle exists in nature for survival. This idea Darwin owed to Malthus. If, in the process of random mating, offspring were born with some slight physiological difference—a somewhat more functional beak, a different color by a shade, a minutely more powerful leg muscle—that allowed it better to feed or defend itself in its environment, its chance of survival would be greater than that of organisms without the advantageous characteristics. If indeed the organism did survive, it would pass on the advantageous characteristic to its offspring. This slight advantage had "naturally selected" one organism over another as a survivor. "The slightest advantage on certain individuals," wrote Darwin, "at any age or during any season, over those with which they come into competition, or better adaptation in however slight a degree to the surrounding physical conditions, will, in the long run, turn the balance."

This slow change by natural selection answered the question of how certain animals appeared so well adjusted to their environment. With enough time and enough matings, organisms were bound to improve their ability to get along in a particular environment. Those that were less qualified physiologically were slowly excluded, eventually becoming extinct. The English philosopher Herbert Spencer called this process "the survival of the fittest," an epithet often quoted and which Darwin included in later editions of the *Origin of Species*.

For Darwin, a good hypothesis was one that would explain observable phenomena. To him, natural selection was a theory that explained so many things. The year the *Origin of Species* was published, he wrote Asa Gray: "I cannot possibly believe that a false theory would explain so many classes of facts as I think it certainly does explain. On these grounds I drop my anchor," and then he added prophetically, "and believe that the difficulties will slowly disappear."

The difficulties did disappear, but as so often happened with new, radically different theories, total acceptance is seldom and professional acceptance agonizingly slow. Hooker agreed with Darwin's theories almost completely from the beginning. Lyell at first, despite his own battles with the theologians over time, couldn't bring himself to believe that the concept of evolution as applied to plants and animals was just as valid for man. Darwin won him over with a long series of letters skillfully answering his arguments; finally, in the tenth edition of *Principles of Geology,* Lyell mentioned his acceptance of evolution as a "working hypothesis." He eventually became as strong a supporter as Hooker.

In the United States, Asa Gray thought the *Origin of Species* "masterly" and wrote Darwin that it made "a better case than I had supposed possible." One admirer wrote him, "It has the characteristics of all great natural truths, clarifying what was obscure, simplifying what was intricate, adding greatly to previous knowledge. You are the greatest revolutionist in natural history of this century, if not of all centuries." The influential zoologist Thomas Henry Huxley whose support Darwin anxiously awaited, immediately accepted the idea of natural selection and thought it was stupid that somebody hadn't thought of it before. He warned Darwin, however, to be prepared for the abuse that was bound to follow.

During the first years after publication, the ideas contained in the *Origin of Species* were hotly debated, not only in Darwin's England, but also in Europe and the United States. In England, Adam Sedgwick, to whom Darwin owed his early interest in geology, read the *Origin of Species* with "more pleasure than pain." In addition to its conflict with the doctrines of religion, Sedgwick felt that Darwin had deserted the proper scientific method to reach his conclusions. He savagely attacked Darwin in his review.

Darwin's former mentor, John Henslow, never did adhere to the whole idea but never became one of those who said it was impossible. Henslow died in 1861, in the midst of the controversy. But Darwin's prophecy that the difficulties would eventually disappear proved true. If the controversy never ended completely during his lifetime, he lived to see a general acceptance of the theories and his ideas stimulate new fields of reach. The ability of the *Origin of Species* to inspire the work of others was one of Darwin's fondest wishes.

By inspiring others, Darwin helped put an end to the naturalist of the nineteenth century as a scientific generalist, good at many fields of science, master of none. His ideas led directly to the establishment of ecology—the study of organisms in relation to their environment—as a separate branch of biology. Specific questions that Darwin illuminated helped define botany, zoology, and geology as separate sciences, each requiring detailed research and new methods. The studies of paleontology, genetics, and marine biology all received tremendous stimulus from the work of Darwin. And as he suspected, some of the new research invariably modified his own work.

One such modification came from a rediscovery of the work of the Austrian botanist Gregor Mendel. Though Mendel had formulated many of his theories on heredity about the time the *Origin of Species* was published, his work lay buried in scientific journals until the early part of the twentieth century. Had Darwin known of Mendel's work, it would certainly have changed his treatment of how animals vary through evolution. Darwin, like all biologists then, believed that natural selection produced no sudden changes, the modifications of plant and animal occurring almost imperceptibly during long periods of time. Darwin, like all biologists then, believed that the characteristics of an offspring were a result of blending. That is, an offspring was exactly the median of its parents, biologically shuffled together like the two halves of a deck of cards.

We owe to Mendel the concept of mutation, whereby an offspring could be born with a radically different genealogical makeup than its parents, thus acquiring in one generation a new and different form. Scientists today are still not sure of the exact cause of mutations, but at least the phenomenon was recognized by Mendel. Similarly, Mendel uncovered the fact that characteristics could lie dormant for several generations before reemerging in the makeup of later organisms. Both of these concepts —mutations and dormant characteristics —like additional discoveries have modified the explanations of how organisms evolve. They leave undiminished, however, Darwin's overwhelming demonstration of the fact of evolution.

Publication of the *Origin of Species* in 1859 did not end Darwin's career. In the next twenty-three years the *Origin of Species* went through six editions, the last published in 1872. Each new edition required Darwin's attention. A new, more appropriate example would be added here, a sentence arranged for clearer meaning there. With each edition, Darwin honed the *Origin of Species* into a sharper weapon and, with it, conquered most of its detractors and their arguments.

The following year, 1860, he finished corrections for a new edition of the *Voyage of the Beagle,* the last he would complete himself. Later editions of the *Voyage of the Beagle* are still available, making it one of the most enduring travel epics ever printed. In its own, not inconspicuous way, the *Voyage of the Beagle* was an inspiration to a younger generation of biologists, too, creating much the same kind of enthusiasm for foreign landscapes as Humboldt's *Travel Narratives* had done for Darwin. Alfred Russell Wallace, who had shared the first presentation of evolution and natural selection with Darwin, modeled his book *Malay Archipelago* on Darwin's journal. A younger naturalist, Henry Bates, who once traveled in the Amazon with Wallace, received Darwin's encouragement to publish his experiences there in a popular form. Bates' subsequent book, *The Naturalist on the River Amazons,* received much praise and remains one of the classics on the Amazon and tropical nature. William Henry Hudson was born in Argentina and spent much of his life there, visiting the Amazon and later England, where he became a noted naturalist and literary personality. Hudson admired the *Voyage of the Beagle* greatly, and frequent references to it can be found in his reminiscences of the gaucho and life on the Pampas and in Banda Oriental.

All the while, however, Darwin continued with new

projects. He completed a study of animal and plant variability under domestication and another on the flycatching drosera. He completed a work on orchids and an innovative study on the expression of emotions in animals and man. In 1876 he finished a brief autobiography written especially for his children, with no intention of it ever being published.

Perhaps the most important work after the *Origin of Species* was one in which he tried to develop some of the themes of the *Origin of Species* in direct reference to man. It was inevitable that he would have to take man into consideration, and *The Descent of Man* was published in 1871; it fired some of the most reactionary criticism Darwin had seen since publication of the *Origin of Species*.

In 1881 his health turned from poor to worse, failing completely the next year. He died on April 19, 1882, and a week later was buried in Westminster Abbey a few feet from the grave of Sir Isaac Newton.

Darwin's sailing mate from the *Beagle,* Captain Robert FitzRoy, continued his erratic ways after the *Beagle*'s return. In 1843 he became for a short time the governor of New Zealand. But his impatience and temperament didn't fit the assignment, and he was relieved a few years later, returning t o England. There for a while he found himself. He established England's first meteorological service and contributed a great deal to scientific weather forecasting. His constant harangue, furthermore, succeeded in convincing the Admiralty to substitute the word "port" for "larboard" to signify the left-hand side of the ship, ending forever the similarity and confusion between "larboard" and "starboard" in the nautical vocabulary.

With publication of the *Origin of Species,* FitzRoy became one of Darwin's most emotional critics, if never an influential one. At one scientific meeting where the idea of evolution was discussed, FitzRoy stalked the back of the meeting room, waving a copy of the Bible over his head, saying that there was only one authority on evolution, the Book.

The financial troubles that began with the purchase of the *Adventure* stayed with FitzRoy until the end. Years later the Admiralty admitted that many of FitzRoy's on-the-spot purchases had indeed saved money in the long run and that perhaps their refusal to pay was unjust. It came as a satisfaction only to his relatives. When FitzRoy died by his own hand in 1865, a public subscription was taken to pay his debts.

The *Beagle* outlasted both Darwin and FitzRoy. For some years after the voyage to South America, it stayed in service, continuing survey work through the 1870's, when steam replaced sail. The *Beagle* was finally sold out of the British Navy a few years after Darwin's death and ended its sailing days as a training ship for the Japanese Navy, finally being broken up in 1888.

In his brief autobiography, Darwin found it surprising that a man possessing "such moderate abilities" could ever have become so powerful an influence on the scientists and science of the time. He vowed that he owed his success to nothing more than extraordinary powers of observation, industry, a love of natural science and "the ambition to be esteemed by my fellow naturalists." What he had no doubt in believing, however, was that the whole course of his life resulted from the voyage aboard the *Beagle*:

. . . yet it depended on so small a circumstance as my uncle offering to drive me thirty miles to Shrewsbury, which few uncles would have done, and on such a trifle as the shape of my nose.

EPILOGUE

The Third Voyage of the Beagle

IF THE *Beagle* were to sail today, Darwin would perhaps fill as many pages in his diary as he did more than 130 years ago. There are new things to see. The continent of 10,000,000 people then will soon have 200,000,000. The present combined population of two cities —Buenos Aires and Sâo Paulo —are larger than that of all South America during Darwin's time. The years that elapsed saw a birth of modern South America, and much of what Darwin would see today would have little relation to South America during those first years after independence. Yet there would be some things that he would recognize.

In Brazil, the red soils found beneath the tropical semideciduous forests have been the country's great resource, equal to all the gold and silver taken from the Andes by the Spanish. They account for less than 5 percent of Brazil's land area, although admittedly that is 5 percent of a gigantic piece of geography. Almost all the tropical forests that once covered red soil have been cleared to make use of the fertile soil. Darwin could still find great tracts of tropical rain forest along the rivers of the Amazon Basin and a few other places where temperature and rainfall are high enough. But the tropical semi-deciduous forests are gone.

For most of its history, there was no limit to Brazil's resources, or so it seemed. Now, with the best and most accessible soil in use, the country is faced with a problem: which land to use next. Outside the tropical red soils, the rest of Brazil is too jungly, too hilly, too infertile, or simply too much trouble to get to. Despite industrialization, which is happening in Brazil faster than in any other South American country, it is still an agricultural nation. Forty percent of the world's coffee and large quantities of cacao, sugar, and tobacco are raised on a small portion of the country's land.

Added to limited amounts of fertile land is a growing number of people. With 90,000,000 people, Brazil today is twenty times larger than the Brazil Darwin visited. It is already by far the largest country on the continent. The distribution of the population mirrors the pattern during Darwin's time. Four-fifths of the people live near the coast.

The unpopulated parts of Brazil cover an extent unimaginable except by flying above them, hour after monotonous hour, or traversing them by boat for weeks.

Today, unlike a century ago, the most desirable areas are crowded with crops and people. The vast frontier inland is Brazil's future, if only the people are willing to endure the hardships of developing it.

One scheme to shift the population inland was changing the capital to the planned city of Brasilia, 800 miles in the interior. Before its founding, Brasilia's site was truly in the middle of nowhere, in the sparsely inhabited outback of Brazil named the Mato Grosso. It is still too early to tell whether the attraction of the capital will drive people inland in sufficient numbers. Another area of Brazil that has never responded to development is the Amazon Basin. The region of tropical rainforest, except for a few brief years of rubber boom, has never been a source of wealth for Brazil. Yet geologists believe there are vast quantities of minerals and precious stones lying beneath the jungle-covered land.

During his last day at Salvador, Darwin entered a comment in his journal which perhaps holds the key to Brazil's future as well as any written today: "If to what Nature has granted the Brazils, man added his just & proper efforts, of what a country might the inhabitants boast."

One thing Darwin would not see in Brazil today is slavery. Slavery was abolished in 1888, Brazil being the last Latin American country to do so. The *fazendeiros,* needing inexpensive labor, fought abolition until the end. By 1888 so popular was the cause for ridding Brazil of slavery that the actual passing of the law was greeted by all except the planters, with dancing in the streets and eight days of festivities, followed by what one contemporary writer called "a delirium of enthusiasm." Still reigning, Dom Pedro II called the abolition of slavery the greatest happiness of his life.

With freedom, some former slaves took to the hills to eke out a meager but free existence; others chose to continue as paid workers on their former *fazendas,* living much the same life as before. A few plantations of coffee, cotton, sugar, and tobacco, faced with new costs, gave up or just went broke. One of the quickest reactions to the abolition of slavery was the stimulation of immigration from Europe.

For all South America, the second half of the 1800's was the great era of European migration. The countries that benefited most were Brazil, Argentina, Uruguay, and Chile. Spain, Italy, and Germany contributed the largest number of immigrants in those years, with small groups coming from such tiny places as Switzerland and Wales. Before slavery was abolished, the immigration to Brazil had never in its greatest year exceeded 30,000 people. The year following abolition, 97,000 immigrants entered the country, mostly Italian. In 1891, two years later, the figure was 102,000. Most of the new immigrants headed for the coffee country, centering in São Paulo. With coffee pouring out through São Paulo's port of Santos, and immigrants pouring in, the city expanded. Coffee, immigration, and the impetus of Brazil's newest boom —industry —have built São Paulo into the largest, fastest-growing city in South America, although Buenos Aires also claims to be first in size. The Italian influence in São Paulo is strongly apparent.

The city of Salvador would probably ring a note of

nostalgia for Darwin. It remains a tropical city with a certain nineteenth-century charm. The influence of the Negro is stronger in Salvador than in any other Brazilian city, with Rio a close second. But in the overall composition of Brazil, the Negro is being absorbed. Today, less than 10 percent of the Brazilians are pure Negro, a distant statistic from the years when three out of four Brazilians came from Africa.

The next country that Darwin visited has more resemblance to the land he saw than one would expect after more than a century. Uruguay, then Banda Oriental, is still a country whose main occupation is exporting meat and eating it. Sixty-six percent of the land is grazed by livestock, except that today sheep have been added to cattle. The people of Uruguay export most of their meat. But along with the Argentines, they eat more meat each year than any other people on earth.

Another first for Uruguay is the size of its capital compared with other cities. Uruguay is a one-city country; Montevideo's population is a little more than 1,000,000 people, the next largest city scarcely one-tenth of that. Maldonado, the tiny village near where FitzRoy overhauled the *Adventure,* is an unimportant city, except that three miles distant, among the sandy dunes where the *Adventure* was careened, now lies Punta del Este, one of South America's most luxurious resorts.

The gaucho still exists in Uruguay, more than in the other countries visited by Darwin. The gauchos are not quite as bloodthirsty as they were then, but just as proud and highly admired.

If the *Beagle* followed the same route, Patagonia, at least its northern fringes, would be Darwin's next stop. More than any other place, Patagonia would look the same as during his visit. The land has changed little, the time since Darwin's visit being but an instant in geologic history. Without man's action one way or another, little change could be expected. Oil was discovered in the 1950's at Comodoro Rivadavia, situated between the mouth of the Río Negro and Puerto Deseado. Today, with 50,000 people, it stands as the largest and most important city on the coast of Patagonia.

The interior remains almost uninhabited: the Indian tribes that once subsisted there are a fraction of their former size, relegated to life on reservations. Patagonia is a national territory of Argentina, much the way Alaska before the days of statehood was related to the United States, but in every way much less important. Only the Amazon Basin equals Patagonia in its lack of penetration or interest by modern man.

One other thing that is unchanged is the dispute over who owns the Falkland Islands. After the construction of the Panama Canal, there was little reason to round the Horn. Subsequently, the Falklands lost all importance. Today the islands are occupied by a few thousand immigrants from England, who make their living raising sheep. Argentina still claims the Falklands, but not so strongly as to interrupt the continuing trade between the two countries. The Argentine government, however, refuses to allow the importation of any book or map that refers to the islands as anything but the Malvina Islands belonging to Argentina.

A present-day Patagonian. The Indians have been rounded up and now live on reservations. The interior of Patagonia and the Amazon Basin remain the two least-known parts of South America. COURTESY AMERICAN MUSEUM OF NATURAL HISTORY.

Once, after the *Beagle*'s voyage was finished, Darwin saw Argentina's former dictator, living the life of a country gentleman in England. Considering Rosas' career after Darwin met him on the Río Colorado, it was a surprising way of life. Rosas returned to power in 1835, becoming the model of a nineteenth-century dictator. His picture hung in every home: his secret police spied, bullied, and assassinated. Those who were loyal —and who would not be? —were obliged to show allegiance by wearing red ribbons or a red sash. He quarreled with France, then with England. He blockaded the river traffic to Paraquay, trying to force the small country into Argentina's realm. For all of his ruthlessness in crushing the regional rebellions and *caudillos,* Rosas brought Argentina its first unity as a country. He was finally ousted in dictator-like fashion by an army led by one of his trusted lieutenants, though unlike most dictators, he escaped dying by the sword he would have been quick to use himself. In 1852 he fled to England, living there until his natural death twenty-five years later.

The half century following Rosas brought Argentina and the Pampas into its own. In 1878 the Conquest of the Desert, surely one of history's most calculated wars of extermination, succeeded in ridding Argentina of all its Indians, except in Patagonia. In 1877 refrigerator ships were introduced, which gave a boost to a beef industry that spread over the Pampas, owing mainly to British investment, and a railroad system that converged on Buenos Aires.

Lastly, a great wave of immigration brought 2,000,000 immigrants from Spain and Italy before 1914. The great majority were farmers. Unlike the *estancieros* of a former era, the new immigrants planted wheat and corn, which not only fed cattle but were exported to the rest of the world. Today Argentina ranks as a top world exporter of beef and grains, still an important supplier to England and other countries of Western Europe.

After a short era of minor importance, Tierra del Fuego has again become one of history's backwaters. Despite what has happened since his visit, Darwin would probably find it little changed. In the late 1800's a coaling station was founded at Punta Arenas, at a spot first visited by the *Beagle,* on the north side of the Strait of Magellan. Before the opening of the Panama Canal in 1914, nearly every ship bound from Europe to the Pacific stopped at Punta Arenas. It was also a minor sheep-raising center after sheep were introduced from the Falkland Islands in 1865. In 1945 oil was discovered across the strait, in Tierra del Fuego proper, the first boost since its decline began from the opening of the Panama Canal. The city now is a major oil-export center, and with about 65,000 people the largest and southernmost city in Chile.

Early in this century Tierra del Fuego was divided politically between Chile and Argentina by a special commission formed by King Edward VII. The larger chunk went to Chile. The city of Ushuaia in the Argentina part, overlooking the Beagle Channel, is advertised as the southern most city in the world, though Chileans, not to lose face, have a naval weather station on the shore directly across the Beagle Channel to the south.

The Indians of Tierra del Fuego are nearly as primitive as when Darwin saw them. There are fewer of them, however, and at least one tribe has become extinct. The charts for the Strait of Magellan used by the *Beagle* for a third voyage would be based on those made by FitzRoy between 1826 and 1835.

In the unimaginable length of geologic time, the 130 years that have passed since the *Beagle* visited the west coast of South America are no more than an instant. The west coast remains a geologically active region, subject to periodic violent earthquakes. Concepción and the coast for 300 miles south were racked by a more intense earthquake in 1960 than the one Darwin observed in 1835. The city was devastated and the landscape torn by the shock. Lakes appeared where once there had been farms, and huge tracts of land were elevated many feet. Lima suffered another serious shock in 1966. But earthquakes have not been enough to ruin the prosperity of Chile or Peru, as Darwin predicted. New construction methods have made factories and office buildings less susceptible to earthquake shock, although each earthquake takes its share of homes and the shacks of the poor.

Following the *Beagle*'s visit, nitrates became the economic foundation of modern Chile, the vast bulk of exports going to Europe. World War I was the beginning of the end for Chilean nitrates when the Germans, cut off from their supply, learned how to make a synthetic product as good as the original. For Chile's economy it turned out to be a disguised blessing. A major problem in the economy of many Latin American countries is their dependence on one crop or export for their economic health. A slight change in the demand for cotton, coffee, bananas, or sugar is enough to cause a depression in any such country. The decreasing demand for nitrates forced Chile to develop other industries. Most notable in modern Chile is copper. Next to the United States and the Soviet Union, Chile is now the third largest copper producer in the world.

Chile shares one great problem with almost every other South American country. The land-granting systems of the Spanish and Portuguese gave away most of the prime agricultural land to favorites of the crown. In many countries, those lands are still owned by the descendants of these first settlers, although now there are millions more people demanding land on which to live and earn a living. The problem of land reform is one of the biggest issues in South America today, something equal in importance to the civil rights struggle in the United States.

Five of the Galápagos Islands are inhabited now, with a total population of about 1,500 people. Shortly after Darwin left the islands, the Ecuadoreans founded a prison on Chatham Island, which gained a terrible reputation. It was closed in 1958. Owing to the fame the islands received from Darwin's accounts, they have become a minor tourist attraction, and once a month steamers leave the port of Guayaquil for a fourteen-day tour of the islands, all of which now officially carry Spanish names.

Like the buffalo of the Central Plains of the United States, the great tortoises that Darwin studied have nearly been hunted out of existence. Presently a few thousand of them are kept on a special reservation on Santa Cruz, formerly Indefatigable Island, operated by a foundation not surprisingly named after Charles Darwin.

From the Galápagos the *Beagle* would sail west, on around the world. In Tahiti, New Zealand, Australia and the islands of the Indian Ocean, Darwin would find much of the old mixed with the new. What he might have noted in his diary we can only guess.

BIBLIOGRAPHICAL NOTE

DARWIN was in many ways his own best biographer. An admirable introduction to the public man and much of the private is *The Autobiography of Charles Darwin,* an abridgment of an earlier work, *The Life and Letters of Charles Darwin.* Both were edited by his son, Francis Darwin, and contain an autobiographical sketch, a reminiscence of his father written by Francis, and a number of letters written and received by Darwin. The former contains fewer letters, omitting the more scientific. A later volume, *More Letters of Charles Darwin* by Francis Darwin and A. C. Steward, supplement these.

A number of formal biographies have been written, and Geoffrey West's *Charles Darwin: A Portrait* remains one of the easiest to read and most authoritative. Something briefer is *Charles Darwin* by Ruth Moore.

Of the specialized biographies, Sir Gavin DeBeer's *Charles Darwin: A Scientific Biography* is an eminently readable, straightforward introduction to Darwin's scientific contribution. Loren Eiseley's *Darwin's Century* discusses Darwin's forerunners and some of the modifiers that came later. It contains a particularly complete discusion of Mendel.

As for Darwin's scientific works, the most pertinent to this book is the *Voyage of the Beagle,* first published in 1839. For intimate detail on his everyday life during the voyage, there is *Charles Darwin's Diary of the Voyage of the Beagle,* edited by his granddaughter, Nora Barlow. The *Voyage of the Beagle* was based on his diaries, and the wealth of personal comment make this one-volume edition of his diaries in some ways more lively to read. Many editions of the *Origin of Species* and *The Descent of Man* are still available, as is a new edition of *The Structure and Distribution of Coral Reefs,* which proposed a theory of how atolls are formed. Some insight on the friendship between Darwin and FitzRoy can be found in H. E. L. Mellersh's recent biography *FitzRoy of the Beagle.*

About South America: The standard, scholarly, geographical work is Preston James' *Latin America.* Smaller and more descriptive is *Latin America: A Geographical Commentary* by Irmgard Pohl and Josef Zepp. This is a translation from the German, neatly edited by Kempton Webb.

Two brief surveys, both available in paperback, provide in their separate ways fine introductions. *Latin America* by William Lytle Schurz is a fact-packed descriptive survey of history, geography, government, and economics, while George Pendle's *A History of Latin America* is a smoothly written, analytical history, particularly strong on the countries of southern South America.

The Growth and Culture of Latin America by Donald Worcester and Wendell Schaeffer is a dependable, thorough work emphasizing the economic and political history of Latin America. A newly published cultural history filled with rich and colorful details is *Latin America* by Germán Arciniegas.

Two unique approaches deal with two separate eras of Latin-American history. William Spence Robertson's *Rise of the Spanish America Republics* tells much about the fight for independence and the years immediately following, mainly through fine sketches of the men who achieved it. Frank Tannenbaum's *Ten Keys to Latin America* is a finely written discussion of modern Latin America and why it is the way it is.

One of the most popular literary forms of the 1800's was the travel book. It exists about the countries of South America by the hundreds, many of these in English, as a result of the close trade connections between England and South America throughout the nineteenth century. They vary from the frothy and near fraudulent to the sober and scientifically detailed.

One very objective account of Brazil just prior to independence is Henry Koster's *Travels in Brazil.* Henry

M. Bates' *The Naturalist on the River Amazon* was mentioned in Chapter 12 as a classic of its type. The feeling of life in Argentina and Uruguay is best captured by William Henry Hudson in *Far Away and Long Ago* and *The Purple Land.* A well-done contemporary collection of many writers, including Darwin and others, is Frank MacShane's *Impressions of Latin America.*

Index

221

Indians, 12, 13, 19, 26, 34, 47, 52–53, 78, 88–90, 94–96, 108, 114–17, 120, 121–22, 128, 133, 154–55, 170, 177, 208, 210, 211–12; wars of extermination, 115, 125–27, 129, 210. *See also* Incas
Ithacaia, Brazil, 67

Jaguel, Chile, 158
James, Preston, 216
Jemmy Button, 89, 90, 94, 95–96, 144–45
Jenyns, Leonard, 20

Keeling Island, 12
King, Philip, 15, 30, 186
King, Philip (son), 30, 50, 59, 76
King expedition of 1826, 15, 18–19, 85, 88, 89, 94
Koster, Henry, 217

La Paz (schooner), 85, 98
Lamarck, Jean Baptiste, 36–37
Las Minas, Uruguay, 105, 107
Las Conchas, Argentina, 134
Latin America (Arciniegas), 217
Latin America (James), 216
Latin America (Schurz), 217
Latin America: A Geographical Commentary (Pohl and Zepp), 216
Laurie, Mr., 66
Lavater, Johann Kaspar, 31
Lawson, Mr., 182
Lennon, Patrick, 64, 66, 69
Libre (schooner), 85, 98
Life and Letters of Charles Darwin (Francis Darwin, ed.), 215
Lima, Peru, 119, 160, 170, 175–78, 212
Linnean Society, 191, 193
Loa River, 172
London, England, 33
Lyell, Charles, 72, 73, 74, 88, 131, 165–66, 167, 186, 187, 190, 191, 192, 193, 196

MacShane, Frank, 218
Madre de Deus, Brazil, 70
Magellan Channel, 151

Malaria, 76
Malay Archipelago (Wallace), 199
Maldonado, Uruguay, 98–99, 100–13, 207
Malthus, Thomas, 189
Malvina Islands. *See* Falkland Islands
Maria I, Queen, 63
Marine biology, 197
Mastodon, 132, 134
Matthews, Reverend, 89, 94, 95–96, 183
Megatherium, 130, 131
Mellersh, H. E. L., 216
Mendel, Gregor, 197–98, 216
Mendoza, Chile, 165, 168, 188
Mercedes, Argentina, 136, 137
Minas Gerais, Brazil, 62
Mining in Brazil, 54
Montevideo, Uruguay, 80–81, 82–84, 87–88, 100, 111, 136, 137, 207
Moore, Ruth, 216
Moors, 52, 57
More Letters of Charles Darwin (Francis Darwin and Stewart, ed.), 215
Mount Chimborazo, 26
Mount Orsorno, 162
Mount Sarmiento, Tierra del Fuego, 151
Mutation, concept of, 198
Mylodon, 132

Napoleon I, 17
Naturalist on the River Amazon (Bates), 199, 218
Natural selection, concept of, 189–90, 192, 193, 194–97
Navarin Island, Tierra del Fuego, 90, 94
Newton, Sir Isaac, 200
New Zealand, 12, 183, 214
North Wales, 27

Origin of Species (Darwin), 12, 13, 185, 190, 192, 193–99, 216
Orinoco River, 26

Pacific Ocean, 151, 152–53

223

South America, 12–13, 203–14, 216–18; British interest in, 17–18, 63, 86–87, 98; cattle industry in, 86, 100–3, 115, 210; copper mining in, 171, 172, 213; gold mining in, 62–63, 172; immigration from Europe, 206, 210–11; silver mining in, 79, 170–71, 172–74, 176; slavery in, 26, 50–53, 56–57, 58, 67, 69, 126, 205–6; wars for independence in, 16, 17, 80, 115, 135–36, 155, 178; wars of Indian extermination in, 115, 125–27, 129, 210

Spain and Spaniards, 16, 17, 47–48, 78–79, 114, 115, 138, 143, 154, 155, 175, 176, 180, 204, 213

Species, theory of, 112, 185, 186

Spencer, Herbert, 195

Steward, A. C., 215

Stokes, Mr., 34, 85

Stokes, Pringle, 19, 146–48, 149, 152

Strait of Magellan, 16, 88, 150–51, 211, 212

Structure and Distribution of Coral Reefs (Darwin), 216

Sugar industry in Brazil, 54

Sydney, Australia, 183

Tahiti, 12, 183, 214

Tannenbaum, Frank, 217

Tehuelche Indians, 126

Tenerife, Canary Islands, 27, 42–43

Ten Keys to Latin America (Tannenbaum), 217

Tidal waves, 162

Tierra del Fuego, 12, 15, 18, 34, 38, 85, 88–99, 144–45, 146, 150–51, 153, 156, 211–12

Tordesillas, Treaty of, 47

Tortoises, 180, 181–82, 213–14

Toxodon, 132, 134

Trafalgar, Battle of (1805), 16

Travel Narratives (Humboldt), 199

Travels in Brazil (Koster), 217

Tucumán, Argentina, 119

Uruguay (Banda Oriental), 77, 79, 80–81, 82–84, 87–88, 98–99, 100–13, 122, 206, 207, 218

Ushuaia, Argentina, 211

Uspallata Pass, Chile, 168

Ussher, James, 72, 73

Valdivia, Chile, 163

Valdivia, Pedro, 155

Valparaiso, Chile, 153, 154, 159, 165, 168, 169, 172, 175

Venezuela, 155

Vespucci, Amerigo, 47

Volcanoes, 162

Voyage of the Beagle, The (Darwin), 13, 186–88, 199, 216

Wallace, Alfred Russell, 192–93, 199

Warspite, H.M.S., 75

Waterman Island, Tierra del Fuego, 90

Watertown, 23

Webb, Kempton, 216

Wedgwood, Josiah, 28, 188

West, Geoffrey, 215

Whaling industry, 18, 180

Whitley, Mr., 169

Wickham, Mr., 44, 85, 154, 160, 175

Woolya, Navarin Island, 94

Worcester, Donald, 217

York Minster, 89, 90, 94, 95–96, 144–45

Zepp, Josef, 216

Zoonomia (Erasmus Darwin), 36